YOU AND THE UNIVERSE

YOU AND THE

By N. J. BERRILL

UNIVERSE

WITH SUPPORT FROM

Walt Whitman

DODD, MEAD & COMPANY, NEW YORK, 1958

To M. J. B.

J. M. B.

E. J. B.

M. E. B.

About This Book

The title of this book obviously embraces more than can be grasped by any human being, let alone encompassed within these covers. The discussion here presented is restricted to the scientific outlook, although at the end the scientific and the spiritual find their common ground. Such understanding as we have is new, and only now is it at all possible to bring together the universe, as seen by astronomers and astrophysicists, and life as understood by biologists. The writing of the book has been difficult and the subject does not always lend itself to easy reading and from its very nature can never do so. The human problem is stated in the first chapter and the answers, such as they are, are given in the last two chapters. It will help to have read these first, before the book as a whole is undertaken. Each of the intervening chapters deals with one particular aspect of life or the universe. Altogether they lead to the final chapter and give it substance.

CONTENTS

NOW WE ARE ONE

"But before Man," asked Jonah, shocked out of his wits. "Do you mean you understood nothing at all? Didn't you exist?"

"Certainly," said God patiently. "I have told you how I exploded in the stars. Then I drifted for aeons in clouds of inchoate gas. As matter stabilized, I acquired the knowledge of valency. When matter cooled, I lay sleeping in the insentient rocks. After that I floated fecund in the unconscious seaweed upon the faces of the deep. Later I existed in the stretching paw of the tiger and the blinking eye of the owl. Each form of knowledge led to the more developed next. Organic matter led to sentience which led to consciousness which led inevitably to my divinity."

"And shall I never call you father any more? And will I never hear you call me son again?" asked Jonah.

"You may call me," said God, agreeably, "anything you please. Would you like to discuss semantics?"

So Jonah found himself alone on the road to Nineveh. And yet he was not alone. For the gourd was with him, and the lungfish, and the stars. He knew that he was a man who had come out of the sea. And he knew that he was a man who had come out of the sun. And in Nineveh he took root, and he flowered in the expression of his consciousness until he died.

—From "Jonah" by Irene Orgel

WALT

"Sail forth—steer for the deep waters only,
Reckless O Soul, exploring, I with thee, and thou with me,
For we are bound where mariner has not yet dared to go,
And we will risk the ship, ourselves and all."

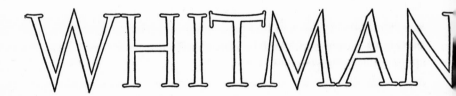

WHITMAN

1 : THE PREDICAMENT

Just what are we doing here, spinning on a tilted planet swinging round a star?

The question rings persistently whenever we cease to listen to the babble of human voices and the clamor of contemporary life, for it dwarfs all else with its insistent call for an answer. Where do we stand, with our few pounds of flesh and bones and our fleeting lives? The question is old and has been heard in one form or another ever since man became man. Yet only a short while ago we were all God's children, holding most of His attention, and the world was exclusively ours for better or for worse. The sun shone to give us warmth and light, the moon to bewitch us, the stars were there to be born under, and the volcanic depths to serve as hell. Now paradise is lost and we find ourselves in limbo, inhabiting one of the minor planets of a middle-class star drifting in the outer arm of a spiral galaxy no different from a hundred million more that are visible through our telescopes. Space and time and stellar

3

systems are overwhelming and to face the twinkling sky of night with any sense of what you see requires either courage or a great amount of faith. Stars are no longer baleful or beneficial, and have no concern with us, but they leave a lonely terror striking at the heart. So here we stand, looking wistfully into the void and nostalgically back into time, for knowledge has put us outside our house. Can further understanding re-open the door? That, at least, is our hope. Perhaps in the end we can rediscover the reality of our home with a greater sense of wonder and a more mature appreciation.

Now that we have found the universe can we find ourselves within it? Is all this immense machinery of physics and chemistry the essential thing, with man and his fellow creatures an incidental by-product tarnishing a planet's bright surface, or is this animated fuzz that we call life the crown and glory of creation? Collectively and symbolically we are either all-important in the scheme of things or of practically no importance at all. This is a question of values, certainly, but it is one that can be examined in a rational way.

Against the vast scale of energy, matter, time and space now confronting us, the total quantity of earthly life appears pitifully small. Even in terms of the earth alone, all that lives is little more than a smudge on the surface of the land and a little discoloration of the film of water. We cannot challenge the cosmos except on terms of our own. Yet that we can do.

We can look at the problem in two ways. What does a sun amount to without a living planet to nourish at its side, and what is a living being that we should pit its worth against a stellar furnace and the universe at large? These are not rhetorical questions but are such that can be examined and answered as matter-of-factly as in any other field of scientific inquiry. We should realize, too, that we live in a materialistic society, in an age of mass production and high-velocity transportation of men and missiles and may very well be overimpressed by similar phenomena taking place outside our system, for such emulation may flatter us and make us obsessed with our own prowess.

Tied in with it all is the question of universal life, not merely human in relation to nonhuman life on this planet, but the occurrence of life and what may grow out of it in planetary systems elsewhere in the universe. If ours should be the only planet sustaining an intellectual, emotional and spiritual life —in other words, if we and our lowlier companions are the only sentient beings in the universe, then too much has gone into the making of too little and none of it makes sense. On the other hand, if we can show that life is most probably widespread throughout creation, with potentialities at least as great as we possess, then the whole picture changes and we can look upon ourselves as citizens of the universe and no longer as lonely souls wailing at the edge of darkness.

Modern astronomy is awesome enough under any circumstances. With man missing from the view it is frightening. Yet man is missing only because we ourselves have left him out. You can't see him through the telescope because the telescope is his own and he is looking through the other end. In fact, we have the curious situation where a part is trying to encompass the whole and is rather belatedly now becoming self-conscious about the attempt, for nature includes all of the universe and man is not only a part of nature, he is in it up to his neck. Above the neck, of course, everything tends to get mixed up, for there lie both the universe in the mind and the mind in the universe. We in our conscious selves see both outwardly and inwardly, though rarely both ways at once; and this may, in fact, be the source of much of our difficulty—

the need to join outward observation with inner intuition, to bring the essence of science and the heart of religion into one harmonious whole.

Our immediate problem however is to find man's place in nature in the widest context. It is the aim of science to co-ordinate all observable phenomena within a single natural order and it is its faith that such is possible. Hence the basic objection to acceptance of the supernatural. If the scientific stand is justified, then everything, whether of matter, energy, mind or spirit, belongs to one vast scheme—it is all one and every part has meaning in relation to the whole. This is as much a tenet of faith as any other belief, but it forms the working hypothesis of all real scientific endeavor. As a basis for action or inquiry it is worth pushing to the limit, with our models of the universe and man in the universe continually undergoing construction and reconstruction as information and understanding steadily increase. If facts or phenomena, in whatever field, fail to fit in, then we modify or rebuild our conceptions until they do, on the assumption that they belong and that there is no separate pigeonhole for mystic revelation and no possibility for arbitrary intervention by any powers that be. If this brings the divine down to earth, so much the better for earthly inhabitants.

Man is made of matter, turbulent with energy, in continuous action while he lives. Whatever else he may be, he has substance to begin with and this is where we start. Step by step, for there are no safe short cuts, we can probe the nature of life and matter and the stars. If they have meaning only with reference to one another, this should become discernible.

WALT

"I am the Poem of Earth, said the voice of the rain,
Eternal I raise impalpable out of the land and the bottomless sea,
Upward to heaven, whence vaguely form'd, altogether changed,
and yet the same,
I descend to lave the drowths, atomies, dustlayers of the globe,
And all that in them without me were seeds only, latent, unborn;
And forever, by day and night, I give back life to my own origin,
and make pure and beautify it."

WHITMAN

2 : WIND AND WATER

The face of the moon is clear and dry. No wind stirs the dust, no water runs off the crater slopes, no seas lie between. The bright side is hot, the dark is cold—no atmospheric veil shields the moon from the sun or from the blackness of space at night. No moisture is present to swell a seed, no air for even a slug to breathe. What gas or vapor may once have been has long since vanished, too lightly wedded to too light a body for anything more than a brief connection.

The earth is different. It is larger and heavier, with a great metallic core, and the pull of gravity at its surface is six times stronger than the moon's. The lighter stuff at the surface is held well in place and only the lightest matter of all, naked hydrogen and helium, escapes into space from the outermost fringes of the atmosphere.

The atmosphere is vital in every way. Most of it is nitrogen, inert but comforting and perhaps in changed or unchanged form a left-over blanket from the making of the planet. The rest is mainly though not entirely oxygen, of somewhat peculiar origin. We feel the air but slightly, it is true, unless the breezes blow or unless we travel faster than our natural pace. Yet without its unfelt weight we would leak at the seams and our eyes and ears would pop. The pressure is there whether sensed or not.

Apart from nitrogen and oxygen the air contains both water vapor and carbon dioxide, two compounds present in relatively very small amounts but with tremendous potency. Together they form slightly acidified carbonated water which falls as rain or mist to dissolve the minerals from the earth's stony crust and carry them down to the oceans. And so mountains erode and seas get saltier.

Thus we begin. In the air and water around us we find four of the lightest and most active elements in creation—hydrogen, carbon, nitrogen and oxygen. Taken singly, at the temperatures at which we live, three of them are gases and the other a fine black powder. Taken together they seem to hold much of the secret of the universe. This is chemistry, certainly, though of an apparently simple sort. Look at it for a little while, for it tells a story and shows the road to beauty.

Carbon for instance may be the soot on the face of a chimney sweep, or the slippery graphite in a pencil, or the hard crystalline brilliance of a diamond. The single element in its purest state can yield different forms, can be hard or soft, and be as clear as light or black as pitch. Under different conditions different properties emerge, yet all are there waiting to be called forth by the magic wand of circumstance. This perhaps is the key. Under what circumstances does matter unite in such a way as to become alive and at long last even to think about itself? To find the answer takes us far afield.

Crystals, whether diamonds produced in the cooling of

molten rock spewed up from deep in the earth's crust, or snow falling from clouds on a chilly winter day, or any of the host of various colors and forms found in nature or laboratory, have a symmetry we recognize as beauty and all have the property of growth. For crystals do grow, adding layer to layer on each facet or plane, keeping the lovely form but growing ever larger so long as the raw materials are available and conditions are right. Snow crystals are often astonishingly large, floating down to earth like feathers, and show the most elaborate patterns. And still they are but atoms of hydrogen and oxygen united as molecules like those of water vapor or of liquid water itself, though linked together in a distinctive way.

In the snow crystals the molecules stand in rigid arrangement one to another to form a tracery of design that we can see. At a little higher temperature they let go and slide about as water, almost as incompressible but free to run wherever gravity beckons and a path is open. This in reality is the state that concerns us most. Water crystals, whether of ice or snow, may be beautiful, but they spell death to living tissue. Water vapor may help to keep us from drying out to some extent but has otherwise little meaning. Water itself, cool water especially, is both the medium of life and the matrix of life and there is nothing anywhere to compare with it.

That is a sweeping statement to make but so far as chemists and physicists can tell, it is true. Water, as a liquid, has properties which are unique. It is for instance the only liquid that becomes lighter when it freezes, so that ice floats on seas and lakes and insulates the water below from further cold—to the comfort and survival of anything alive in the depths. Water also holds more heat and loses it more reluctantly than any other liquid. It can dissolve a larger variety of substances in greater concentration than any other liquid. No other liquid known to science approaches it as a solvent or as a stable medium. In virtually every way it stands alone in chemical eminence, bathing and penetrating every living cell on earth. The question is whether any other substance might serve instead?

The answer is no! Nothing we know of other substances suggests that any of them could take its place. The chemical world, especially in its less complicated forms, has already been pretty thoroughly explored and the properties of most simpler substances, liquid or otherwise, are well known. The answer still holds. Water is unique and its qualities and peculiarities enter so intimately into the very matrix of living material that we cannot imagine life in any other terms.

How wet and what sort of wetness is a living thing? Wetter and more mysterious than you think! We ourselves are comparatively dry and are not the best example to start with. A jellyfish living out its life in the salt ocean is closer to the primeval state, although it also is as much a citizen of the contemporary earth as a buzzing bee or a bombastic human. Yet more than ninety-seven percent of a jellyfish may be water, with only about three percent comprising the mineral salts and carbon compounds that make the difference between the substantial symmetry we recognize as jellyfish and some formless water to quench our thirst.

Even a man is nearly three-fourths water, including of course his blood but also his bones. A pinprick anywhere starts a leak; a burn makes a water blister; the sight of good food makes you drool; and a sad or sentimental thought brings damp tears to your eyes. You have to take in, either as drink or as water in your food, at least two quarts of water each day to maintain yourself. Nor is this just a case of staying wet, of bathing your tissues or satisfying your thirst. Water has been traced through the body by substituting and following heavy water which can be recognized, the same kind of heavy water employed in the making of hydrogen bombs and perhaps the future source of an unlimited supply of energy for human needs and fancies. What it shows in mammalian bodies is that the water taken into the living system is incorporated into actual living substance, at the same time displacing water already present. For a while, at least, water becomes alive in a mysterious way, different from what it is under other circumstances, and these properties of water in living substances are only now beginning to be understood. If we are sure of anything it is this, that liquid water is the basis of all earthly life and that it pervades living matter through and through as its mother substance. And we have no reason whatever to suspect that a substitute exists elsewhere in the solar system or anywhere in the visible universe.

If this be a fact, and it is as certain a fact as most of those we base and build our lives on, one consequence of much significance emerges. Water as we know it, as distinct from ice or water vapor, can exist only within a very narrow range of distance from a star.

At sea level water turns to steam at 100° centigrade and to ice at zero, but whether we use this scale of temperature or the Fahrenheit scale more familiar in everyday use which says water freezes at 32°, we are using a purely arbitrary scheme that says little about the place of liquid water in the cosmic scale. Keeping to centigrade degrees however, which is customary in science everywhere, absolute cold, where nothing happens and even the atoms are still, is 273° below the freezing point of water. This is absolute zero. On the other hand, on the same scale extended in the other direction, hydrogen fuses to form helium to give rise to the explosion of a hydrogen bomb at a temperature of several hundred million degrees, a momentary heat to be sure but nonetheless real. This is a temperature typical of the interior of a star, so high that matter itself is in a remarkable state and elements change from one kind to another. The point now, however, is that on this tremendously extensive scale taken as a whole, water can exist as such in only an extremely narrow range not far from the lower end, and that a little too near or a little too far from its heat-giving star, water on a planet turns to steam or ice. Even then, if conditions on earth are significant, life belongs only to the lower half of that little range of temperature. If there is meaning here, it is of remarkably delicate precision.

Above all, perhaps, water means movement, action and vitality, the antithesis of solid rigidities, yet with all a firmness and direction not found in gaseous stuff. Our own dryness and hardness are mainly an illusion, for we still have the capacity to splash when fallen from a height. For first and foremost every living thing, on land, in the sea or in the air, is water vibrating with life—not water alone but water most of all, together with a little dust. Such water and dust in living form combine in some subtle way, so far but little understood, the crystalline symmetries and the essence of liquidity.

WALT

"*Nothing is ever really lost, or can be lost,*
No birth, identity, form—no object of the world.
. . .

To frozen clods ever the spring's invisible law returns,
With grass and flowers and summer fruits and corn."

WHITMAN

3 : DUST OF LIFE

What is a man? From one standpoint he is flesh and blood, brains and bones. But so are catfish, bats and toads. Were it not for our bony ballast even the worms who at last devour us would have to be included, for substantially speaking we are all of a kind.

Three-fourths of the atoms in living matter consist of oxygen, about ten percent is hydrogen and another ten is carbon, with nitrogen but a little over two, and the long list of the remaining elements make up less than one-fiftieth of the whole. Put together in the proper way and we all turn out to be a rather weak watery solution of salts and carbon compounds, more or less jellified. You and I, with all that we eat and the various bacteria, fungi and viruses that live so happily within us, are a mingling of the wind and water and dust that constitute the surface of the earth. The miracle is that such stuff as we are made of should walk and talk and know such things as song and sadness.

17

The dust of life is disconcertingly like powdered granite and limestone, although the differences that do exist have meaning. Oxygen makes up the bulk of even the hardest rock we stand on, bound tightly into its crystalline structure but predominant nonetheless. In our bodies it is joined mainly with carbon and hydrogen and our substance is practically combustible. All it needs is a little drying out. Yet in the harder rocks the oxygen is tied mostly to silicon and aluminum, two elements conspicuously missing from our own constitution. Otherwise the minerals of the rocks are the minerals of our tissues, present in much the same relative abundance. Those that are rare on earth are rare in us, but for the most part what is abundant on earth is made the most of.

The difference between stone and flesh may seem to loom large in this elemental sense and that is true enough up to a point. Yet it boils down to the question of water. The silicates which comprise the sandy deserts, the feldspars of the mountains, the curbstones and headstones, all those irresistible natural objects that bruise and bury human flesh and hold it down, barely dissolve in water at all—which accounts for their bulky presence in the landscape and their virtual absence in water wherever we find it, whether in lake or ocean or the juices and tissues of living creatures. Some organisms in the sea do manage to pull out and concentrate silicon, to be sure. But it is difficult or more would do it and even at that the material is used only for making insoluble skeletons, in the glass sponges of the animal kingdom and in the microscopic diatoms of the plant world. In terms of minerals we and the rest of the living are chiefly what is most abundantly dissolved from the rocks by water. Minerals that don't dissolve reach neither the sea nor the salts in our bloods and, conversely, minerals which are rare in the earth, even if soluble, are rare in cabbages and kings as well.

Silicon and aluminum, so common in the ground, we lack. Carbon on the other hand, though thinly spread through air and rock and water, forms the living framework of living things. We drill for oil and mine for coal for carbonaceous fuel, yet all like this that burns has at some time been alive. To call the living world a canopy of carbon compounds is little exaggeration, for their variety, complexity and interrelatedness in living matter is almost unbelievable, while outside of the living we find merely a little carbon dioxide in the atmosphere and carbonates in limestone and ocean. For carbon is the exception to the rule of accessibility. It is as though a magic hand had caught up the water and the carbon of the earth and cast it back as living scum—call it creation if you will, but a creation with a present force as well as ancient history.

To label this rich mantle of life a scum is not to belittle it. In a purely spatial sense it is even less, for if you picture the earth as a disk several feet across outlined in pencil, the thickness of the line includes all but the highest mountains and greatest ocean depths. Five miles up and down from the mean surface of the planet is hardly noticeable against the almost eight thousand miles of its diameter. Yet this slight irregularity of the crust with a little moisture clinging to the lower levels is not the film of life itself but the whole range within which life can exist. In fact, our living scum is not even a scum but a discontinuous smattering of carbon complexities concentrated close to the actual junction of air with land and water. Fly a few miles above this surface and look down and only a greenish tinge here and there remains to indicate the living world— no distinctive vegetation and nothing of the animal world at all. All life together adds up to only a minute fraction of the earth's dusty surface, with most of the heavier components left out altogether.

In this literal manner of speaking I am myself less than the dust, merely a selection of the lighter stuff of the surface put together in a peculiar way, and the same statement holds for everything else that lives. This is the crux. In terms of material quantities we are next to nothing. Yet where else but on the surface of a more or less solid globe could its substance find freedom to writhe and grow and blossom and fly? Where else can the rays of a sun-star reach to stir up a dance of life? It can happen at a planet's surface or not anywhere at all.

The power switch lies in that greenish sheen covering the lower and moister parts of the land and adding a little off-color to the desert blue of the oceans. For apart from some purple in certain bacteria, the green chlorophyll of plants is the pathway from light to life. Without it all life is cut off at its source. Even as a piece of scientific sleuthing the chlorophyll story is dramatic, involving as it does the use of radioactive carbon as a tracer, though it is much more than that. For, granted that the primary stuff of life consists of chemical compounds of carbon, hydrogen, oxygen and some nitrogen, united in various ways, and that a tremendous tonnage of carbon dioxide drifts through the atmosphere with additions from every volcanic eruption, not to mention the great mass of hydrogen and oxygen comprising the liquid ocean, no amount of shaking the one with the other will produce much more than carbonated water. The materials are there but they are already happily united in their existing forms and are joined in matrimony by the strongest bonds known in chemistry. Life, in fact, is not something set in motion long ago to get along as best it can ever since, whether by some sort of divine intervention or a peculiar concatenation of circumstances: it must be maintained and incessantly driven along its path of freedom, hour by hour and year by year throughout the ages, coerced into being from moment to moment and forced willy-nilly into the channels of time.

The power is light. No wonder man is and apparently always has been a sun worshiper or that plants struggle upward and turn with the clock. And power there is in plenty. Sunshine falling every day on each square mile of the planet's surface carries almost as much energy as in the explosion of the first atom bomb. Some of it is reflected as earthshine, brighter than moonshine; most of it is absorbed as heat by land and sea; but a little is intercepted by chlorophyll, mainly in the small round green plastids most plant cells possess, and converted into chemical energy. For what? To break the bonds of water and set free the hydrogen in its active form—the simplest and most potent of all the elements and the building block for all creation. Once divorced from the oxygen, the hydrogen is immediately combined with carbon dioxide and away we go. This is where the radioactive carbon tracer is used as a detective to follow these otherwise secret activities. The astonishing discovery is the speed at which events follow one another, for within a few seconds the simple carbon dioxide is converted into sugars, with phosphorus atoms acting as an essential go-between. And so sweetness is brought into the world and the chain reaction continues and one thing leads to another, all reacting together to some extent and producing pyramids of increasing chemical complexity.

What of the oxygen so ruthlessly split from its union in water when the light rays strike? Some of it is burnt with part of the sugar to supply further energy to drive the plant's chemical machinery but most of it escapes into the atmosphere. In fact, in the course of a year the vegetation of the earth sets free about four hundred billion tons of oxygen during the process of uniting some twenty-five billion tons of hydrogen with one hundred and fifty billion tons of carbon. We should be impressed at the scale at which living matter is manufactured. And as a chemist once said: "Without that sugar and oxygen there could be no thought, no sweet sonnets of Shakespeare, no joy and no sorrow." For the sugar made in the green tissue of plants and the oxygen in consequence poured into the air between them supply the fuel that keeps the animal world in existence. We burn them together to give power to our heart and muscles and energy to the mind.

This is no more than a sketchy beginning and leaves out the nitrogen which makes up four-fifths of the air we breathe. Nitrogen is essential to the construction of all proteins and all hereditary material, to the most vital of all living substance, yet what we breathe of it does no good. The situation is even worse than the Ancient Mariner who saw "water, water everywhere nor any drop to drink." Sugars and starches, together with the fats so readily made from them, for beauty or for worse, are all very well but they do not supply the building blocks for growth itself. These are the amino acids, about thirty kinds, the almost infinite combinations of which, strung together in various assortments and relative numbers, give rise to all the proteins and to the fundamental differences between one living being and another and even one part and another. Nitrogen is indispensable to all of them. No nitrogen: no growth, no maintenance of nerve or tissue, nor anything but a slow demise.

Changing the matter of the earth's surface into a consuming living motion apparently is no easy task. Look back for a moment! Water is all about, carbon dioxide is plentiful enough, while gaseous nitrogen bears down to the extent of one hundred and fifty tons on each acre of the earth. Leaving aside the lighter metals and minerals which also enter the living systems, three more or less unwilling or indifferent partners are forced into intimate and potent unions. Solar radiation is needed to pull asunder the two components of water. Phosphorus, present to only one-tenth of one percent of the earth's crust, is necessary to carry the energetic hydrogen to its new destiny with carbon in the cell. Once brought together the union seems joyful enough, but nitrogen, so overwhelmingly but inertly abundant, seems almost incomprehensibly reluctant to enter the living society of elements. Only as nitrate can it enter in, or as an ammonium salt, which raises a problem. A little nitrogen may be changed to nitrate when lightning discharges in a thunder cloud, though this is not certain, and the only sure source of nitrate or ammonia comes from the action of bacteria, which in a sense is cheating since it raises the unanswered question like that of the chicken and the egg: which came first?

To some degree at least the picture has cleared a little, putting aside this last conundrum. The four lightest of the common elements—hydrogen, carbon, nitrogen and oxygen, to list them in the order of their atomic number and weight—are brought at last into unions of tremendous complexity by the blazing radiation of a star, by the rare scintillating genius of phosphorus and perhaps by the spark of lightning. No elements occur in living tissue that are not found outside close by and those mainly used are among the most abundant. The heavier elements that lie without are employed with great discretion, for as a rule when they do get in they create much havoc. Altogether, in this elemental sense, none of us is unique, and out of dust and water we grow and to water and dust we return, our secret lying in the sun and in the pull of the earth. Without the power line from the sun all the machinery of life would come to a stop. Without the heavy cores of the planet within, neither water nor air would remain in sufficient amounts. Without such filmy envelopes the primary stuff of life itself is gone. So with a sun for radiance and a planet for growth, and a certain distance in between, then only does life have a chance to show its face.

We can take a step further, tentatively at least, and say that if the phenomenon we recognize and know as life is the natural expression or the consequence of the way the elements of living matter are strung together—and science at least knows no evidence to the contrary—then life in all its fantastic forms, actions and potentialities is as much a property of the basic stuff of the universe as the matter and energy of a starry furnace. There is more wonder and significance in such a view than in calling in some strange vital principle to mark off the living from the nonliving or in evoking the whim of a special creator.

At the same time the manner in which life is awakened by the action of a sun on a planet appears to be chancy and wasteful yet exquisitely precise, with the product a wonder to behold, much as though the genie had been called forth by rubbing Aladdin's lamp. Magnitude and power lie with the sun but the miracle of loveliness lies here at hand. Planets like ours with a fragile film of life, rather than the stars that support them, may be the real jewels in the heavenly crown.

WALT

"Who includes diversity and is Nature,
Who is the amplitude of the earth, and the coarseness and
sexuality of the earth, and the great charity of the
earth, and the equilibrium."

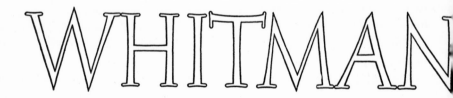

WHITMAN

4 : THE ONENESS OF LIFE

When you look around at nature, whether on land or lake or sea or in your own backyard with its weeds and bugs and flowers, its diversity seems overwhelming. If you add to it all the various germs that lay you low from time to time, and the fungi now used as antibiotics to save your life, not to mention the various odds and ends of parasites that plague us and our pets and our crops, the unity or oneness of earthly life is difficult to see. Yet we do see it. We see a different face in every human being, yet behind them all we see the same person whether their skin be yellow, brown or white or whether they be men or women. The diversity is there without a doubt but so is the essential oneness. Nobody seriously questions the family of man or the fundamental brotherhood. In fact the present human problem, though by no means the only one, is how to accept and adjust to the all-pervading diversity in such a way that the underlying unity predominates.

If we look farther and deeper, however, a greater unity becomes apparent, a unity with all of nature that primitive man with his intimate association with the living world around him felt instinctively. Cities and highways of stone now bar the way and what once was felt almost as an emotion must now be found and acknowledged by the understanding mind instead. There is no other way except for the more favored few who can still escape to, or live within, the wilderness, or what remains of it.

Nature is one, with ourselves included. Few people, perhaps, would deny this, yet I doubt whether more than a few take in its full meaning—it is too easy to give lip service to the thought and to feel it is yours for a light caress.

To begin with, of course, there is unity in death, when dust and moisture so recently alive return to the earth from which they came. The material components, apart from some differences in relative amounts, are the same no matter who or what it is that died. Yet even more striking than this substantial agreement is the way the atoms and molecules are put together in the living organism, whether to make an animal, a plant or a lowly bacterium. At this most difficult of all levels of inquiry, where biochemistry and biophysics meet, where the structure and activity of matter stagger the scientific imagination, where the magic tends to disappear at the touch of the investigator's finger, the very complexity itself says as strongly as anything can be said that it is all of one kind. Simple things may crop up independently of one another and yet be much alike, but likenesses seen among extremely elaborate concoctions, such as identical twins or triplets, are taken at once as evidence of true relationship and a single origin. This is how it stands with the stuff we call protoplasm, whether of a human brain cell or a malaria parasite.

In all there are much the same proportions of mineral salts, one to another and in their relation to water, much the same ratio of carbon compounds to the rest, and essentially the same kinds of carbon compounds everywhere, consisting mainly of sugars and starches, fats and proteins—in all animals and plants and the inbetweens. There is a very peculiar feature, too, in that whereas most carbon or organic compounds may be lopsided or screwed either to the left or to the right, and can be manufactured either way in the laboratory, in nature they all have the leftward twist, as though God blew once from one side only.

All along the line we find the same features showing through the murky surface. Bacteria, fungi, fireflies and fish, for instance, with many others, all produce living light, a kind of cold blue-green light called bioluminescence, produced in every case by the action of an organic ferment upon a protein. The living chemistry is fundamentally the same whether the light is an accidental by-product of bacteria growing on decaying flesh or a deliberate device for making sexual assignments among insects or fish. Animals digest the proteins in their food by means of certain enzymes, but plants have the same enzymes in their tissues and we even extract them from the fruit of the papaya for use as tenderizer on tough roasts of meat. In fact, when we get down to details, we find that all the protein matter of living tissue everywhere, animal or vegetable or only half alive, consists of the same few kinds of amino acid building blocks, put together in various proportions and combinations, and that the variety of life comes mainly from this playing around with numbers.

To go a little further, both plants and animals can manufacture cellulose from sugars, although only a few animals manage it while all plants do so and make the most of it. Even the materials mainly responsible for heredity are built around a single complex and unique compound of carbon, nitrogen, hydrogen, oxygen and phosphorus known as nucleic acid and present in all, from polio virus to daffodil and ape. And much the same sort of statement can be made about many other outstandingly complex chemical substances in living matter, such as the pigmented compounds responsible for handling of the oxygen for tissue respiration. The list is unending and running through it all is the same marvelous chain of energy transfers, involving phosphorus compounds, which underlie the action of all muscles whether of elephants, flies or sea anemones; the activity of the living, rhythmically beating hairs that bring mucus up from your lungs; drive a bacterium through water or a sperm to an egg; or the machinery that divides a cell into two parts. Everywhere we turn the same paradox emerges: beneath all the diversity of living things the essential oneness of living material shines brightly, and wherever we see unity with all its strikingly plain meaning, it is inevitably clothed in diversity. The more life appears to be the same the more it seems different, and the more scintillating the differences the more do we see it as a single event of awesome grandeur and wonder, of which we are ourselves so obviously a part.

And just as a craftsman may be judged by his work so living protoplasm may be judged by what it can do as well as by what goes on within the living cells as such. And what it can do is plenty.

Putting first things first, perhaps, the stuff can grow, increasing its own peculiar substance at the expense of raw materials from the outside world. But then so can a crystal, which is not alive by any reckoning so far adopted. Yet protoplasm not only grows, it grows old and it dies, though usually leaving some small fragment of itself to start the process anew. Growth, age, death and rebirth by some means seem to be universal properties. Even the so-called immortals, the single-celled plants and animals that are forever growing and dividing and cease to exist only in consequence of some environmental hazard, are not really immortal. Whenever such an individual divides into two, it dies as an individual and two others take its place. Life and death are inborn together from the start, setting the stage for joy and tragedy before ever the curtain rises.

When a cell, any cell, divides to form two daughter cells, the separation is the climax of one event so fantastically intricate and yet so precise that the minutest idiosyncrasy of that particular cell is passed on through the channels of time by the parade of cell generations almost ad infinitum. No event outside a living cell can match the amazing manner in which it divides. A cell may be small and generally invisible to the naked human eye, yet its component molecules run into billions and as a self-sustaining, self-perpetuating unit of the universe it is something to be reckoned with. For there is little doubt that free-living single cells existed and slowly perfected themselves for perhaps a billion years before the first many-celled plants and animals came into being.

In any case, the living cell, whether a solitary adventurer in the microscopic world of a drop of water or a wandering phagocyte in the human blood stream, or a nerve cell, or a cell at the tip of a blade of grass, is sensitive to the universe without. I doubt that the importance and potentiality of this single quality can be ever overestimated. From it stems the reaching of a tree or a flower toward the light, the moth to a flame, or a man for his mate or the moon. It leads to the writing of this book, to the scanning of distant nebulae and to the search for God.

If there is truly a unit of life, the cell is it. In its heart lies the secret of mortality and such immortality as the earth can bear. Its outer layer quivers with sensitivity and emergent motion. Chemicals shatter or stimulate its surface. Contacts make it writhe, contract or expand. Gravity pulls on any part a little denser than the rest. Light attracts or repels it, so that it either moves or grows according to light and darkness, and life in general moves toward the sun at dawn and shrinks away at dusk, pulsing with almost every change the star induces. Here half seen in latent form lie all that we associate with the living kingdom—vision, nervous energy, vital action and reaction, sensibility and hunger, growth and beauty, for as the size of living organisms increases to larger and larger dimensions and may consist of cells numbered in the multibillions, the basic sensitivities become eyes and brains, protoplasmic writhings become the hands of men, and gravity becomes the magnet we fight against.

Time and again the same things emerge as life enlarges. Red blood pigment, muscles, hearts, limbs and feelers, all crop up in sporadic occurrence in the animal kingdom, in more or less unrelated groups, yet all no more than elaborations of the various qualities all cells possess. Leaves of the mimosa tree cringe at touch, the evening primrose opens at dusk, eyes emerge in insect, octopus and frog and many others, no two of them the same, and wings and fins have appeared in wind and water on several separate occasions. Organs of balance, heavy stones set in sensitive capsules, respond to gravity in jellyfish, snail, eel and shrimp, essentially the same in form and function but independently evolved. And roots grow down. All because protoplasm is what it is—excited and suffering from cosmic causes.

Turn everything backward, both the rose and the maid, and one by one the branches unite in the course of time to join the single trunk of life, with its roots in soil and water. One in all and all in one describes it well. For such is life, that it flowers in diverse forms but grows from a common spring and is a state of matter that has formed upon the earth but once and for all. The evidence confirms this and none denies.

WALT

"Long and long has the grass been growing
Long and long has the rain been falling
Long has the globe been rolling round."

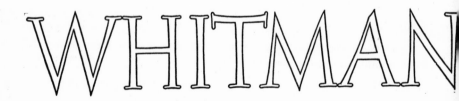

WHITMAN

5 : A HOUSE OF CARDS

Life in the world about us at first glance consists of animals
and plants large enough to be seen individually and counted
without too much difficulty—the trees, shrubs, flowers, birds,
sheep, cattle, dogs, cats, perhaps a few horses, not to mention
the more or less successful crossers of our hard-surfaced highways. If you do get out of the car to hunt or fish or merely to
wander in the woods without murderous intent of any kind,
wilder forms may flit or skip before you. When you recall what
you have seen in nature or in books life seems to range from
small to large, from insects to elephants and whales and from
blades of grass to great sequoias. Even on this scale both mice
and men belong to the upper classes, and humans together
with their domesticated animals must be rated among the
giants.

A giant of any kind requires substantial support. A hump-
back whale, for instance, which is far from being the largest
of its kind, needs a ton of herring in its stomach to feel com-

35

fortably full—as many as five thousand individual fish. Each herring, in turn, may well have six or seven thousand small crustaceans in its own stomach, each of which contains as many as one hundred and thirty thousand diatoms. In other words, some four hundred billion yellow-green diatoms sustain a single medium-sized whale for a few hours at the most.

Food chains of this sort link most of the larger active animals with their basic food supply and the column widens toward the base. Not only do the numbers of the supporting organisms increase with each step down but so does the actual quantity of living matter compared with that of the more grandiose creatures nearer the top. The larger and the more elaborate the creation the more expensive it becomes to make and maintain.

In our own case, leaving out the water we drink in any form of liquid, every individual in North America, for instance, consumes on an average about thirteen hundred pounds of food a year or nearly forty tons in a lifetime, all for the sake of a single human life. If all the food is converted into terms of vegetable material the tonnage is almost doubled. And so it goes! Every large animal, and the flesh-eating kinds especially, is maintained at relatively enormous cost by lesser forms of life. Short cuts, of course, are always possible where, by certain techniques of food-capturing, the middle part of the chain is eliminated, though they merely highlight the dependencies. The largest whales and the largest sharks feed on shrimps and even smaller marine crustaceans, sifting them out of the vast volumes of water that are taken into the mouth, the one through baleen sieves or whalebone hanging like curtains from the roof of the mouth and the other by gill-raker sieves at the inner opening of the gills. On the other hand, the great, toothed sperm whales feed on giant squids almost as long as themselves when tentacles are included, which in turn feed on fish that feed on crustaceans that feed on diatoms and other microscopic forms of life. Altogether the upkeep of any one of the giants is costly beyond measure and where the rate of growth is forced, as in the larger whales, the cost is compounded. When a blue whale is born after nine months in the womb it is already twenty feet long and after another two years measures seventy feet and is ready to breed, though it dies of old age before it is thirty.

In the case of the largest trees it is mainly a matter of time. The giant redwoods are not remarkable for their growth rate or for their demands for mineral nourishment. Their secret lies in their power to endure, to go on growing at a general pace for several thousand years. Yet, in the end, when you multiply the yearly intake by the number of years of life, the total maintenance for a redwood is again a colossal figure.

Life, however, should not be measured by the number of monsters and monuments produced in such striking forms. In unseen ways the meek already inherit the earth and apparently have always done so, though some are not so meek as others. Insects outnumber everything else together, both in actual numbers of individuals and in numbers of species, for the most part feeding directly upon vegetation and in turn forming sustenance for the majority of birds and many other creatures. Yet the lower does not exist for the sake of the higher-ups. Grass is grass for the sake of being grass for as long as possible. Insects live out their fleeting lives at their own level, for the benefit of neither birds nor bats nor even spiders. Each platform in the scale of life is a shimmering vibrant vital level of existence and lives by its own right, just as do the supporting acrobats of a vaudeville pyramid. In nature, in spite of the astronomical number of minute beings required to sustain the life of a giant, only a small percentage of them unwittingly supports the individually larger but numerically fewer elect.

Right at the bottom, tangling up the roots, so to speak, are the bacteria, far smaller than any single-celled plant or animal. They far outnumber everything else, both in the soil and in the sea, and given the chance can outgrow it as well. Even as it is, biologists have estimated that the bacterial organisms of the earth outweigh the rest of life by twenty to one, though they are generally invisible and a century ago their existence was not even suspected.

In a purely quantitative sense the total amount of living substance has been estimated both for the continents and the oceans. Somewhat surprisingly the two values are much the same and it dampens our enthusiasm to realize that the seas are no less exhaustible as a potential source of food than the already overgrazed land. In each case, the total is about fifteen billion tons of living carbon present from moment to moment. Altogether, this may seem a lot, especially when we add the other components of living matter to the scale. Water itself perhaps may be left out of the picture since apart from arid regions it is not in any way a limiting factor, but other substances, particularly nitrogen, raise the total considerably. Analyses of the green and yellow photosynthetic pigments of the microscopic pasture plants of the seas show that for roughly every forty parts of carbon, there are seven of nitrogen and one of phosphorus; and there's the rub!

What limits the growth and quantity of the plant life, whether marine or terrestrial, and all that depends upon it directly or indirectly? The sea gives the answer. It is not the carbon, for while carbon dioxide in the air and ocean is limited it is far in excess of what is utilized in making living organisms, and there are hidden reserves as well. The limitations are nitrogen and phosphorus, in their usable forms of nitrates and phosphates.

Recent oceanographic expeditions have accurately determined where and how much active photosynthesis goes on in the oceans. Obviously the process occurs only within the depths to which light can penetrate in sufficient intensity, but even where the water is clearest this is only the uppermost three hundred feet, a very shallow layer compared with the thirty thousand feet of the great depths. Moreover, where the seas are clear and blue, as they are in the Sargasso Sea of the North Atlantic and across the greater part of the Pacific Ocean, they might as well be desert, for clear blue water is empty and the seas, like the land, must show green if they are fertile. In a green sea pasture, the main load of life lies within the upper hundred feet since light can effectively penetrate no deeper. And in the last analysis the key to abundance is the phosphorus. Phosphates are present in extreme dilution and when they are used up, no further growth of plant life can take place and new life must wait for old life to die and turn back some of the phosphorus to be used again. Only where there is a constantly upwelling of relatively phosphorus-rich bottom water, as in the Humboldt current off the west coast of South America, can a rich marine life be sustained at the surface. When this happens, everything grows abundantly, for there is a goodly supply of all the other ingredients of life—and so diatoms and crustacea multiply without end, building up through fish to birds and whales, while on nearby land even humans dig up the excrement left by the superabundant birds and use it as fertilizer for farms and gardens.

The total mass of life, whatever its forms, is limited. That is an inescapable fact—limited in space to a thin smear on land and little more than that below the surface of the sea, and limited in quantity by the amount of phosphorus available as phosphates within immediate reach. The forms that life takes may fluctuate with the season and the geological period, but the total remains the same. Whatever is in shortest supply holds it down, whether phosphorus, nitrogen, water or light itself. In temperate- and higher-latitude winters, when the days shorten and the sun's rays strike at low angles through the atmosphere, the living machinery slows for lack of power rather than for any lack of raw material. In the seas this is the time when the phosphate in the upper layers is replenished by mixing with deeper water brought up by winter storms and also because more of living substance dies than is born. When spring returns the spring bloom is everywhere as increasing light takes up the slack, just as it does on land.

Yet year in and year out, from one pole to the other, the total amount of light falling upon the earth's surface has a very constant value. With very minor fluctuations the quantity of power received from the sun is fixed, for all practical purposes, although only a small part of it is employed in driving life along its course.

Suppose by some means such as an as-yet-unknown process of atomic fusion we could very greatly increase the supply of nonradioactive phosphorus and convert it to a utilizable form for plant growth, would the total carrying capacity for life on earth be much increased? Probably yes, because there is a surplus of all the other necessities. The difficulty would lie with nitrogen since artificial aid in making it available for use would be necessary. Increasing nitrogen fertilizer by itself, which may be possible, is another matter. Adding nitrates to the soil generally brings about greater growth of vegetation, yet alone it merely throws everything out of balance since additional nitrogen increases the living appetite for phosphorus and in the long run more harm is done than good.

As it is, enveloped in nitrogen as we are, no more than a tiny amount gets into the soil and water as usable nitrate and even this mainly through the action of certain bacteria. The nitrogen-fixing bacteria of the soil and sea and in the roots of nitrogen-fixing plants such as beans and clover are practically in control. They undoubtedly carry on this nitrogen-fixing process as part of their own business and not for any charitable purpose. But so long as phosphorus itself does not run short, vegetation and its dependent animal life grows only to the extent that these particular bacteria make possible in their lowly unconsidered way.

Yet somehow each part of the whole system, whether the light from the sun, the water squeezed through the crust of the earth, the dissolved salts, the limited phosphorus, the hard-to-get nitrogen and the bacterial agents involved, all seem to fit together in a remarkable manner. No human engineer would have planned things this way and would have been laughed at had he done so. But the fact is that it works and any interference with the delicate machinery would bring it all to a sudden stop. To say that there is no real system and that the consequences of the existing set of circumstances are accidental and meaningless is to overlook or underestimate their nature.

WALT

"*The hands of the sisters of Death and Night incessantly softly
wash again and ever again this soiled world.*"

WHITMAN

6 : LIFE AND DEATH

The human individual seems to be assailed by dangerous bacteria throughout his life. Babies' bottles and cut fingers must be sterilized, antiseptics are to be seen in every bathroom cabinet, and altogether germs of one sort or another appear to be our downfall. Some, of course, are necessary, to manufacture the all-essential nitrates, to enable cattle to digest grass, or even for a man to make a cheese. Suppose these and their kind were all, with none of the harmful types waiting around to give us blood poisoning or a cold in the head, what then?

The answer is pure horror, although the earth would be without its stench of death. No flesh would decay, no compost heap would amount to anything more than a pile of leaves, and if it were not that viruses might still be around no one and nothing would die except from old age or an accident. Yet death would still arrive at the end of the natural span of life, whether of man or mouse. Accidents would still happen as before and so would organic calamities such as cancer, ulcers and heart attacks. We who had been born would still die and sooner or later so would everything else. New vegetation and new births would appear each spring but each year somewhat less than before. Year by year the living world would shrink a little until at last only a faint suggestion of greenness would be left in watery places, no more than what could be annually produced by the minerals continually and freshly dissolved out of the rocks by falling rain.

The reason is clear. Death without decay ties up more and more of all that goes into the making of life without returning any of the materials to their original source. Dust becomes life without becoming dust again, though it loses its beauty just the same. You see something of the sort whenever you pass an automobile graveyard, one of those symbols of the way things are going. Iron ore was mined from the earth to produce the cars which wear out in a few years and are then junked. Unless the discarded metal is eventually, no matter how indirectly, returned to the shops the raw material will become slowly scarcer, cars will become fewer and more expensive until the annual output is a handful made for only presidents to ride in. The rest of us are back on foot putting calluses on our feet again and taking them off our seats. And so without decay death will leave you as a desiccating mummy just as surely as if you had died in the hot and arid sands of the desert, and the same with everything else from ferns to frogs. If death must come, decay must follow, for otherwise there can be no more birth except for a little while.

We have already seen that the quantity of life on earth is finite, limited, and varying only within a very narrow range. Unless dead life decays and changes back to its original dusty or oozy nature, that amount must be subtracted from the total, a similar subtraction being repeated with every generation until nothing significant is left. On the other hand, if death as well as decay were banished, living things would in effect become immortal and then where would we be? Nowhere, because the situation becomes impossible. If we start with the world as it is now everything would go on living for a while but nothing much could be born or start to grow, since without displacement there could be no replacement, if all the matter that can be alive is already alive. Human beings and other creatures could not continue at all except insofar as they could consume other forms of life as food. Not only new birth but even the continuation of animal life depends on a steady supply of new substance derived from other living forms and the persistence of some life depends too much upon the destruction of other life for immortality in this sense to have any meaning.

With only a limited amount of clay to work with, whatever the models, earthly life must be able to cast and recast continually simply to keep life going, let alone to elaborate the living form or to make changes for the sake of change. Death and dissolution are not penalties inflicted on the living; they are themselves the conditions necessary to the existence of life and they hold all the hope of the future, as they have from the start.

The rate of turnover is fast, faster than we generally realize since we ourselves, like elephants and parrots, somehow manage to live as individuals for a remarkably long time compared with most. For the rest, as a general rule, the smaller they are the briefer their individual existence. Most animals and plants that are large enough to be seen but small enough to be a nuisance live out their lives within a year or but little longer. This is the run of things, in time with the circling of the earth about the sun. For many it is even shorter, with brief lives passing in and out several times a spring or summer season, each in its own exquisitely particular way.

When we get down to rock bottom, so to speak, or at least into the soil and into the sludge of the rivers and the sea, where microbes of every sort abound, including both the nitrogen-fixers and nitrogen-unfixers busy undoing each other's work, and a host besides, the rates of change and exchange are fantastically high. Just how fast will of course vary with how warm or cold the water is, but as long as the means of livelihood are present each microbe grows and divides into two several times in every hour. The innumerable single-celled plants, like the Chlorella that figures so largely in the news as a possible food substitute or addition to take care of increasing human needs, and the equally numerous single-celled animals that feed mainly on bacteria cannot perform quite so well but do not fall very far behind. The point is that with every division two are born and one dies in the sense that the first individual no longer exists even though its substance marches on, usually in different directions. Some have called these unicellular beings immortal, failing to recognize death in any form except material destruction. Even so they are far from immortal, for if all went on living in their descendants the consequences would be quickly apparent.

A microbe or a cell divides into two only when it has already doubled its substance, and if such growth and division occur after every twenty minutes or so, which is fairly usual, roughly ten will be present at the end of an hour when one was there at the beginning. Ten in one hour means a hundred in two, a thousand in three, and if you follow this through a little farther, ten billion at the end of ten hours. Or, since numbers tend to get out of hand, look at the question in terms of weight of microbial matter produced. At this rate of growth and multiplication and in spite of the hardly measurable size and mass of an individual microbe, after two days of such goings on about twenty-four million, million, million million tons would have been produced, which is about four thousand times greater than the mass of the entire earth.

Obviously nothing of the sort occurs, although the potential is there in every microbe, every free-living cell, every organism small and large, given the means and the space and a certain amount of time. Clearly something gets in the way and equally clearly that something is death, not just the loss of individuality in a bit of living substance but death in its final and irrevocable form—chemical death, whereby the elements of living matter return to their native earth, if not in truly naked elements at least as simple chemicals very similar to the raw ingredients. Microbes die almost as fast as they are produced, otherwise the earth would be overwhelmed by them. Yet with every death there is room for another and so the wheels of life keep turning. The king is dead, long live the king, is the cry that has been heard from the beginning of time.

Here, at this microbial level, the controls again are operating. As Pasteur stated it in one crystallizing sentence: but for the work of microbes, death itself would be incomplete. But for the work of microbes life would be negligible to begin with and but for the work of microbes all other life would soon clutter up the earth in mummified form. From microbes to man, the microbes as a group take care of the dead, breaking down organic tissues and substances and, naturally enough, multiplying in turn at their expense. Yet in so doing, whether that which is destroyed is an emperor or the germs that killed him, the old is eventually made over into something new, and so to eternity. Each ethereal structure, whether strutting or not, maintains itself just so long and dies, for no earthly immortality is possible either for individuality itself or for the living substance that expresses it, except through the indirect and subtle form of reproduction. In this light what is remarkable is not that we die so soon but that we live so long. Twenty minutes for a microbe, a few days for a flower, a year for a shrimp or a shrew, but three-quarters of a century for human beings. The progression is impressive and we should not complain.

WALT

"A man is a great thing upon the earth and through eternity."

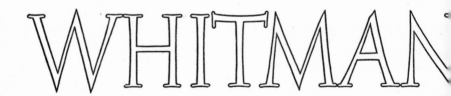

WHITMAN

7 : GIANTS AND DWARFS

From almost any standpoint life, as we know it on earth, is a progression from small to large and from the momentary to the prolonged. The microscopic sustains the less microscopic and so on up the scale to a canopy of giants, until at last there is a falling off in size if not in quality, where cows and pigs sustain mankind and tigers jump at elephants. You see the same sort of picture when you look forward into time, starting from long ago. The first evidence of life in the fossil record, way back in Pre-Cambrian times, again is microscopic. Later on come small fossils, followed by larger ones, not as a steady continuous progression but on the whole with more and more of the larger kinds turning up as time continues. Every group of large animals and large plants has had ancestors of a smaller size, although some large types passed their peak of size some time ago and only their runty descendants clutter up the present earth, such as frogs and salamanders that hide along the water's edge and other damp secluded spots. The largest crea-

51

tures that have left their bones and footprints in the terrestrial mud were dinosaurs and their nearest kin that flourished on the massive continents during the Triassic and Jurassic periods over a hundred million years ago; while great trees of the present such as the redwoods and the giant pines belong more to an older time than ours in spite of their survival into the contemporary world. Elephants, however, run the dinosaurs pretty close and at sea the larger whales overshadow everything that has ever lived, so far as size and weight are concerned.

There are limits to size, as there are limits to height and weight, both for animals and for plants. The limits are set, in part by the nature of the living organism and in part by the earth itself, although so far as we can confidently say that life has been produced from and by the earth, the earth may be said to have designed its own living dimensions. This is no fancy. Even microbes and cells are limited in size by the simple and fundamental fact of existence underlying all living things great and small. You, for instance, whatever it is you really are, are on the inside and your skin draws the line between what is you and what is not you. So with free-living microbes or of blood or tissue cells in your own body. Each is an extremely complex chemical factory bounded on the outside by a surface membrane. Everything that is needed inside must get through the surface and all that is waste must pass through it the other way—and the passageways become crowded. And here nature stubs her toe on one of the facts of life that cannot be avoided: when you double the diameter of a ball, for instance, the surface marking it off from the rest of the universe has increased by four times, but the matter inside has increased by eight. And in terms of cells and bacteria, as enlargement proceeds the jostling at the surface increases far out of proportion to the actual growth. There is but one way out of the jam and that is to divide into two, which has the effect of keeping surface and contents in stable relationship. Here is the reason why all single-celled organisms, whether plant, animal or what-not, must stay as small as they are. They grow, to be sure, but growth leads only to division and so to an increasingly large population but never to large individuals. And so it is with the cells that make up your own tissues. They increase in number as they grow but not in individual size. Your blood cells and brain cells are more numerous than when you were born but they are not any larger. It is the same when you compare a mouse with an elephant. They each have the same kinds of cells to make up their different tissues as do you, and the difference is that an elephant has so many more of every kind than the mouse. Yet a mouse or a shrew represents the smallest and lightest of the mammals and the elephant not only the largest but the heaviest, at least on land.

All these features of the living things have important meaning and signify much, particularly if we ourselves hope one day to stand upon another planet, with or without any expectation of finding other beings wandering around or of even just growing in one place. Single cells, whether microbe, diatom or any other, whether living as free individuals or as parts of something larger, seem to have their limits set principally by their own nature, just like atoms and molecules. But how large a construction can be made of this sort of brick, how many can be put together without the house falling down under its own weight, so to speak, is another question which depends for its answer on the size of the earth.

Have you noticed how restful it is to swim or float in buoyant salt water that is not too cold? Your muscles relax, your heart has an easier time pumping blood horizontally to your head and it flows more readily back from your legs, but above all you have lost your weight or most of it, at least. Gravity still makes itself felt but not to anything like the same extent. When you get out of the water the old aches and pains begin again and you feel your age—gravity is trying to pull you down and is on the verge of being successful. Think what it means to be an elephant!

Much of what an elephant is results from its weight. Put the same bulky body on legs like those of a horse and the whole contraption would collapse on the ground. A pygmy elephant might get away with it but a standard-sized elephant has clumsy, thick pillars for legs because of the weight they have to hold up. It's the same old story. When elephants grew to be twice as big as they used to be, their weight was far more than doubled and legs had to be three times instead of just twice as thick in order to carry the weight. Lungs had to supply several times as much oxygen, hearts had to pump several times as much blood, while trunks still had to reach the ground. Carry it a similar step forward to make elephants twice as high and twice as long as they now are and the absurdity becomes obvious, for the legs would have to be at least three times as thick again as they already are and the body itself would hardly have room for breath, for lungs are essentially folded surfaces exposed to air, surfaces that must also expand three times for every doubling of a single dimension. Such a creature would be rooted to the ground, gasping for air, and unable to move to find the tons of food necessary to sustain it. Not only that, but as a hot-blooded heat-producing object it would suffer an excess of radiator trouble. Even as matters stand now the elephant is naked in order to unload its excess of heat, and with every extra inch in height more heat would be produced inside than there would be additional surface to radiate it away. A mouse has a hard time keeping its home-fire burning hot enough, elephants find it difficult to get rid of the heat they produce, and all because of size. The elephant is the mammalian climax in this sense, though at the other end the shrews outdo the mice. Being the smallest of all they suffer from an excess of surface, lose heat by radiation and convection at a terrific rate and have to eat their weight in flesh each day simply to keep the furnace going, and even then it burns out in about one year.

Great whales, the largest lumps of living matter so far produced, show the truth of all this. Far larger than an elephant— in fact, an elephant could romp up and down inside the inflated skin of a blue whale—they illustrate how much farther size can go under other circumstances. Water supports more than ninety percent of the weight, posture is horizontal with a minimum drain upon the heart, and the radiator skin is water-cooled, a far more effective heat-removing system than the air-cooling mechanism of land animals. Yet even here the limits are set and have been reached. The largest whales must drive incessantly through food-laden waters in order to supply their needs. They cannot, with their particular equipment, drive any faster or more effectively. Intake limits upkeep and to maintain more whale flesh in a single whale would call for the impossible. The peak of efficiency has almost certainly been reached.

Plants are in their own way cut down to size even before they start, just as are the animals. A tree can grow just so high and no higher. Sugar pines and redwoods appear to be the tallest trees that have ever lived or are likely to live. Here again gravity pulls the cord. Leaving aside the hazard of wind, a tree could very well grow much higher without being troubled by its own weight since unlike an animal it has no rickety joints to manipulate. Tree trouble comes in another form—a simple case of hydraulics, for trees live mainly at the top and in any case can grow only so high as water can be raised. Water evaporates from the leaves and to some extent water creeps up to replace it, though the best pump in the world can draw water upward by pull alone to little more than thirty feet. For anything higher some push is required as well, which trees and other plants supply mainly by their roots. Even so, it seems surprising that any form of vegetation can lift soil water to a height of over two hundred feet above the ground. This again appears to be the limit and the great majority of trees, let alone other kinds of plants, are seemingly satisfied with much less.

Gravity not only in part determines the weight of water itself but also the bending and breaking strains of the living structures that attempt to raise it from the earth's surface. Gravity also determines how much atmosphere is held to the earth and this in turn decides how high a water column can be pulled or balanced. Between them, between gravity itself and the atmospheric pressure, both the height of a tree and the weight of an elephant are decided, and in the end we find sizes, weights and heights are closely controlled by the size and density of the planet. Life's dimensions are what they are because the earth is what it is, neither smaller nor larger.

Against the whole scale of life human beings are also giants —not the greatest but great enough. We could grow to twice the height without danger to our bones only by becoming thick-legged and clumsy, and by the same token we could shrink to two feet high only by becoming grotesque. A change in size means a change in shape and we make the best of what we are, as a little lipstick or a razor goes to show.

Against the size of the earth itself, let alone the vastness of the sun or the universe, the largest beast and the largest tree appear to be puny indeed, and so does a man. Against the smallness of atoms and the smaller particles that comprise them, even a microbe is immense, though still invisible without visual aids. Cells that make up animals and plants, though still microscopic, are even larger. The living world, as seen through our eyes without any substitute, lies between the two extremes of the infinitely small and the infinitely large. Yet this is but one way of looking at size.

Stars are larger than you and I, to be sure, and they have an individuality of their own, of a kind, for they have their limits and an active unity, although the same could be said of the ocean; their individuality is at an atomic level, comparable to that of a hydrogen bomb. In the ocean it is molecular and of very great interest, less massive than a star's but with a sort of life of its own, though dependent on a sun and a satellite for its activity. Living organisms are of a different order. For all their activity, or vitality if you prefer, and for all the flux of matter that gives them momentary but continuous substance, they possess unity and individuality to a degree that appears nowhere else. When you consider that an organism, whether it be a rose or a woman, consists of innumerable cells of minimum size and of none too great a variety, it is remarkable that so many can be held together to produce so diversified a being. The numbers involved are too large to be appreciated. A frog's egg, for instance, is neither large nor small, as eggs go, and is rather less than one-tenth of an inch across, yet without taking in any additional material it divides into about one million typical frog cells. If so many cells constitute so small a bit of living substance, how many does it take to make a man? Even the number of cells that compose your brain is so astronomical as to carry no meaning. Yet for all this, the brain is entire and your mind is whole, and your body all in one piece. We can, of course, regard the organism as a kind of cell society or cell state, which not long past was a common way of looking at it, but nowadays such a view has gone by the board and the majesty of the whole, so to speak, appears to be the primary quality, with all cells, tissues and substances as subordinate parts. The wholeness is the essential thing and as an integrated dynamic unit of matter, the build-up from atoms to apes and peacocks is monumental indeed.

To say that a man or a daisy is no more than a highly organized form of matter degrades neither mind nor loveliness— it merely makes matter itself potent with spirit and beauty, though needing the most refined and complicated conditions for their expression. Whatever the import of beauty may be and whatever the significance of human thought and insight may be, neither loses by being rooted in the basic stuff the universe is made of. For beyond matter is—what? The fundamental particles of physicists and what they themselves come out of—something far beyond our present imagination.

WALT

*"Myself through every by-gone phase—my idle youth—old age
at hand,
My three score years of life summ'd up, and more, and past."*

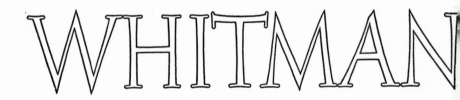

WHITMAN

8 : YOUTH AND AGE

You will never be the same again! The phrase is familiar but its meaning is profound. A man cannot cross the same river twice because meanwhile the river has gone on flowing and though the river bed and the banks may look the same the water is not; and the man is also changed. He may feel himself to be the same person as before but that is only partly true. Time has passed for him as well, and with passing time no man or any beast or bird or fish or flower remains the same. This may be life's tragedy but it is also its essence and it is remarkable that such a flaming, changing, vulnerable creation as a newly made human being can keep its candle burning for so long.

Crystals grow and we find them beautiful. But the growth of a crystal is not life and does not lead to life although living substance has a certain elusive, crystalline quality, which is another matter. Its essential quality, perhaps surpassing all else, goes hand in hand with its perishable nature, for its secret,

61

the very thing that makes it so difficult to capture, is that the exquisitely complex structure that appears before you is almost an illusion. It is there in the same sense that you see a candle flame, although in both cases when the flame goes out something is left that can be buried or thrown away. I have called life a flame, as though this were just a poetic fancy. It is far more than that and all that is lacking is visibility, for as much as anything life is a dance of hydrogen and electrons along the atomic pathways of the body. When the dance and the burning come to an end, life is gone and only the scaffolding remains. And this is no accident.

Any flame must be fed or it goes out. So with life, whether of microbe or man. The living form is the precarious balance struck between the continuous pouring in of the maintaining atoms and the equally continuous falling apart of what is already there. It is like a brick-built house of which all bricks must be replaced from time to time, the harder ones once a year, most kinds once every week, and some very crumbly kinds perhaps every hour. So long as the replacement goes on the house continues to stand. When the labor force begins to tire and the pace to slacken the house begins to show its age. And when the work and all else that goes into the upkeep stops entirely, collapse begins within the hour. This is analogy, certainly, but much the same sort of thing happens to you. In every cell in your body this building up and breaking down continue all the time and a cell lives only so long as it is ahead in the game, although some kinds live only for a matter of days, while others carry on for years. And you, the whole of you which you call yourself, are simply the same sort of balance maintained by the cells. Your blood cells wear out within two or three weeks, old ones are taken apart and more or less tossed aside, new ones are born every second and take their place, and your blood reflects the balance on the credit side. But the radiation you may receive during the coming atomic age may slow down the blood-cell birth rate and call an end to your existence. Nerve cells lie at the other extreme and those you are born with must last your life—they must, since after the age of five, at the most, no new ones are produced and any that wear out will be gone for good. If you fail to die from some other cause before they do wear out, you will become senile and a burden to those around you.

Such is aging, when worn-out cells are replaced more slowly than they decay, when long-lived nerve cells and others replace their living chemicals more slowly than before, when sugars are burnt at a slower rate, when the pace of living slackens. Yet it doesn't start at middle age or at any other age. It doesn't even commence at birth. Aging begins in a human being, as it does in every living being, when the egg first starts to develop. In fact, when an egg divides into two, it has taken the first step on the downward path. From that moment on, no matter how fast it seems to grow, it grows more and more slowly.

The measure of growth is not the number of ounces or pounds put on from one month or year to the next; it is measured by the time it takes to double the weight. On this reckoning a newborn baby doubles its weight very slowly compared with a month-old fetus, but rapidly compared with a ten-year-old child. And the weight you add after the end of your teens is not growth at all but simply ballast of a bulgy kind. In other words, starting from conception, you grow more and more slowly until puberty and then level off. In a sense, you still go on growing but now the cells wear out as fast as you can replace them. Later on they will wear out a little faster, perhaps, and you won't be so quick to replace them, and so on slowly down the hill.

And not only growth. With each beat of your heart, it pumps a little bit less, not enough to measure between one beat and the next but enough to add up in the course of time. With each beat, too, it beats a little more slowly—at birth one hundred and thirty or more to the minute and already slowing down, but at twenty-five no more than seventy, which is the pace you keep up from then onward, although pumping less and less. In a young man of twenty the blood races through the great vessels in twenty seconds, but with every added year it takes a second longer—and the seconds add up and take their toll. Meanwhile, tissues get drier, muscles get weaker and the living machinery begins to creak.

The life of any plant or animal may be likened to a rocket, shot out toward space against the downward pull of gravity. It reaches its greatest velocity almost at once and travels more and more slowly as the fuel burns out, until at last it falters and falls. How far you can soar depends on how fast you start and how slowly your fueling system weakens, which brings us to the question of time itself. How far into time can you go? How far can anything go, anything that is alive?

In a general way, the smaller in space the shorter in time, which is not surprising when you think about it. The life of a microbe is measured in minutes, the life of a free-living cell that feeds upon it usually in hours, for in each case the individual lives until it has grown to almost twice the size it was at first, which takes but a short while for units of life as small as these. At the end of their time they divide into two, which is not exactly death but is certainly the end of the individual. Small creatures one or two steps up the scale of size may live for a few weeks or a few months, depending on how warm or cold their surroundings are. The very great majority of living things of average size, animal or plant, live for a season or a year, not very long it seems, yet immensely so compared with individual microbes. And at the end of their time they die— again as individuals, but not entirely since eggs or seeds continue into time. What was alive still lives, although the individual goes and only a very small part survives to carry on.

Many small lives are consumed in the support of a larger, whether the small lives are those of organisms consumed as food, directly or indirectly, or whether they are constituent cells of the large one itself. In either case small amounts of living time as well as small bits of living matter are added up to make the greater sum, and in the largest and longest-lived forms of life, expansion in space and extension in time go very much together.

The birth of a mammal is a remarkable event that has something of the aspect of a miracle—so much new life is so suddenly present. In a way this is a pity, for the greater wonder is the virtual explosion of the microscopic egg that started some months before the startling advent. Beginnings are rarely noticed, no matter what they lead to, and the beginnings of individual life of every sort are no exception. In fact, most lives begin on such a microscopic scale they are invisible even to the naked eye that looks at them, for the essence of all such beginnings is a single cell—larger than average, to be sure, but generally microscopic all the same. And this is the strangeness of it, a fantastic and unbelievable happening when you pay it full attention, that a minute sphere of living matter smaller than a pin head may expand and expand hour by hour, month after month, and even for many years until it has the bulk and the shape of an ape or a whale or whatever it happens to be. In every second of time the visible beings, large and not so large, vegetable and animal, are growing out of the invisible with a force so subtle yet so irresistible they can break a rock or split an atom. Out of almost nothing came the leviathans of trees and beasts, inexorably expanding to a destined size. Out of almost nothing, almost but not quite—for there is the fact we tend to overlook or take for granted: the capacity of the smallest unit of living matter to grow into stupendous and bewilderingly complicated wholes. It goes on around us all the time; it is the world we live in, and it is ourselves, you and I. We are the event itself, or at least a very significant part of it—giant examples of expansion, marvelously elaborated, and of exceptionally long duration.

Duration is hard to achieve, not that which belongs to crystals and rock but duration of the transcendent form and sparkle that belong to life. Hence the need for continual renewal, of birth from death, of the corn king who dies and the spring queen who brings forth life again. Life is forever being resurrected, not from nothing but from that speck of continuity that breaks off as a bud or seed or egg, leaving the old blown-up construction of the body lagging behind in time to stumble and die. Each fragment that begins anew, no matter what we call it, has time built into it.

In a sense it is like a clock unwinding time according to the power and tension of its spring. No analogy truly serves however, for the reality is a quality of living matter that is fundamental to its nature yet is poorly understood. Examples may be better. A mouse and a man start alike as protoplasmic balls less than one-hundredth of an inch across. Both burn at their brightest at the beginning and each expands with time. But mouse stuff is fully expanded within a few weeks and persists with ever lessening tension for two years at the most. Human stuff expands for about fifteen years, to reach much greater dimensions, and thereafter maintains its weakening vitality for another three-score years.

Giant tortoises, on the other hand, are something else, for the kind of time we are really concerned with is living time, not clock or calendar time. Tortoises and turtles and the vast majority of everything alive, everything in fact except mammals and birds, live at a pace dependent on the temperature of their surroundings and for most of their lives this is much lower than that of the two warmblooded kinds. To make matters equal, the one hundred and fifty to two hundred calendar years of tortoise life should be reduced to a few decades. Even among the warmblooded, inequalities are obvious, for time to a sloth is clearly different from time to a monkey, and a sparrow, for instance, lives literally at a hotter pace than a man.

Perhaps we have here the clue to the true meaning of time. We have clocks and calendars and almanacs, all of which measure the rate of spin of the earth about its axis or the circuit of the moon around the earth or the passage of the earth around the sun. Does it matter? Certainly we find it convenient to divide time of this sort into suitable packages and to be able to designate a particular moment for an assignment with a person or a train or for the meshing of procedures in any industry. Yet all of us feel that this is not a good reflection of time as we ourselves experience it. Childhood days are long and youthful years are eternal compared with the racing sequence of later periods. Time must be measured by how fast things happen—the rapidity of events—and the rate of change. On this reckoning the greatest and fastest happenings of your whole existence took place during the first two or three weeks after you were conceived—everything since then has been comparatively routine and progressively staid. And slow. We should measure the time of our life not by how often a clock can tick while the earth turns completely round but by how much happens to us and in us as living organisms. How often your heart contracted and expanded, how many visual images came to your attention, how many times your interest shifted, how intensely you felt some physical pain and how quickly forgot it, how much joy did you feel and how often did that emotion come to you—how frequently were new cells born and how much memory went into storage. If you have ever watched a mouse with its whiskers vibrant and its nose atwitch, you will have sensed a quickness of living that is faster than your own. Mouse time is not man time, though both are living time. The meaning seems clear: when so-called time is empty, when nothing at all goes on, not even time has meaning. So it comes to this, that living time, which is what really matters to us, is measured by the amount of life rather than by the number of seconds or days or years; and life, being first and foremost activity and action, is to be estimated primarily as energy expended.

There is an initial drive in every egg and seed which carries it through a certain extent of whirring change that we recognize as life. Elements and energy are drawn in as long as the life persists, as grist to the mill, but these are conditions of continuing existence and are not the essence. The essence itself is hard to define but is widely felt and "one crowded hour of glorious life is worth an age without a name" sums it well.

WALT

"Unseen buds, infinite, hidden well
  Under the snow and ice, under the darkness, in every square or
        cubic inch,
  Germinal, exquisite, in delicate lace, microscopic, unborn,
  Like babes in wombs, latent, folded, compact, sleeping;
  Billions of billions, and trillions of trillions of them waiting,
  (On earth and in the sea—the universe—the stars there in the
        heavens)
  Urging slowly, surely forward, forming endless,
  And waiting ever more, forever more behind."

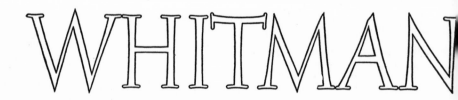

WHITMAN

9 : SO MUCH FOR SO LITTLE

When young Charles Darwin strolled along a Falkland Island shore during the first year of the *Beagle* voyage he came across the spawned egg masses of sea slugs and, having little else to do, took trouble to count the number of eggs in a single tangled cluster. At least, he made an estimate and found it to be more than one hundred thousand. Altogether, along one short stretch of beach, he found minute eggs amounting to several million, a notable quantity in any case yet the more remarkable in view of the scarcity of the sea slugs themselves. The contrast between spawned profusion and rare maturity became a foundation stone in the future edifice of his thoughts. Why so many to produce so few?

Sea slugs are not alone in this profligacy of eggs. A fair-sized cod and a good Virginia oyster can each produce nearly half a billion eggs each season, although in doing so they no more than keep up the preexisting population. If by such means the number of cod and oysters remain much the same year after year, it suggests that anything less would be insufficient. Left alone, the precarious balance of fish in the sea and shellfish in the bays is maintained—a balance easily disturbed by climatic or human agencies—and all seems to be most delicately adjusted, as in a dynamic state of equilibrium. Wherein lies the paradox.

Nature is prodigal without the slightest doubt, as extravagant in her high-handed abandon as any wastrel. Yet efficiency is just as obvious, too, if we can properly speak of efficiency in the attainment of ends that we recognize or label only by virtue of hindsight.

Is it the purpose of nature to produce an adult cod at all, let alone produce one at the expense of casting five hundred million eggs to the ocean currents, to grow at the expense of billions of microscopic organisms? Perhaps, but all you can truly say is that the cod is there. Cod did grow out of the welter of invisible specks and only one cod matured out of so very many that might have done. What of those that did not? Microbes and diatoms can be said to exist in their own right, going about the business of living, growing, dividing and dying, and they could inhabit a world in which no fish was ever seen. But cod eggs, or any other kinds of eggs, that either do not develop all the way, or do little more than start, are another matter. They seem to mean cod or nothing. Is it waste masquerading as purpose or have we here some sort of end in view constructed upon wasteful principles? This is no idle question, for in much the same sense we can ask it of ourselves: are we as individuals thrown up by chance, so to speak, or are we the spear points of a mounting and predestined invasion of space and time?

Predestined, however, does not mean preordained. You as an individual are not preordained to commit suicide, but if by chance you once step off a high cliff or building you are already predestined to arrive at the bottom in a squashy way. So with this build-up to bigger and better beasts, whether cod or oyster or whatever, they may well have been the inevitable outcome of materials and circumstances without implying that they were foreseen in any way, like the beaded bubbles winking at the brim of Keats' heady wine.

The answer to the wasted millions of cod eggs and all the vast majorities of other kinds of eggs is that you cannot take the cod out of the community it lives in and of which it is a part. For then it makes no sense. Likewise, a man out of his earthly context is unintelligible. Our difficulty is to see the system of life as a whole, for its complexity and its dynamic internal relationships are so great. Yet, if we look a little harder, we can see that the cod eggs are not wasted, nor are any other in the long run.

In the first place all those eggs and seeds that fall by the way or begin life without reaching maturity still play a part in the scheme of things. In the sea and elsewhere the general fate of eggs and embryos and young that do not grow up is to be eaten by other forms of life, thereby contributing their substance to sustain and build that of the more successful. Seeds that fall on stony ground are manna for the birds. And at the least they all form food for bacteria and so in the main return as fertilizer to soil and water. In the material chemical sense there is no waste, only the bother of building the stuff up and breaking it down which represent some waste of energy, which may not really matter.

Yet there is good reason for the shotgun technique. The number of eggs or seeds produced by any particular living thing, animal or plant, is a fair indication of the hazards awaiting each one of them. As many are produced as are needed to keep the race in existence generation after generation, otherwise the population would dwindle. For successful propagation of a species there must be an ever-present readiness to exploit every opportunity. And if you want to hit something whose location you are not sure of, you fire a lot of shot in as close to the general direction as you can. So, for the most part, living organisms spawn high, wide and handsome, by one means or another, hoping for the best. So many kinds now struggle to keep a footing on this earth that none can afford to overlook a chance to make good.

Myriads of minute eggs and larval creatures almost as minute drift through the seas, some to stay on as drifters but most to sink here or there to the sea floor, to survive and grow and reproduce or more likely to die—depending on what circumstances they find down below. Seeds are scattered by winds or streams or birds to land no one knows, some to root and grow but for the most part not. Even the air you breathe is an invisible dust of suspended life in the form of microscopic cysts or spores of simple plants, bacteria and animal forms, ready to fall into any liquid medium where their living nature can show itself. When the volcano of Krakatau exploded and covered that island with sterile ashes, as soon as wind and rain cooled and dampened the scorched land, life returned by way of this living dust. You can see it for yourself with the aid of a lens if you leave a little broth standing open to the air. First it will smell; the bacteria have arrived and are busily at work; then a little later larger forms appear that feed upon the microbes, a whole succession of them in fact, all air-borne and ready to come alive at the slightest encouragement.

All of this is but one side of the question. Each living being scatters part of its substance as fragments, which we label as seeds or eggs or spores, because existence is so chancy and something has to survive if the race is to continue. This is good so far as it goes. It goes as far as replacing the passing generation in much the same places and with the same forms as before, so that a pine forest keeps growing where the pine forest was, jellyfish maintain their numbers in the cold northern ocean and worms take the place of worms in the moist soil. Care can be taken that more eggs survive, either by more selective placing or by actual guarding in some form or another, for then eggs may be fewer and accordingly larger. And the larger the egg, or the seed, the greater the likelihood it will successfully grow up. We see the extreme in our own case, where now almost every human that starts to develop lives long and lustily through the years, even if it ends up in a mental institution. Yet if this were all, it would not be enough.

Life, taken as a whole and in all its separate manifestations, is enterprising, not just a business of maintaining the *status quo*. And to be enterprising you have to be different. Here, it seems, life slips into gear and change becomes possible.

Those eggs that Darwin saw on that chilly southern shore were not all alike, no matter how they seemed to a casual inspection. That is the second outstanding feature about any brood of eggs, or milt for that matter, produced by a single individual, whether the individual be a sea slug, a flower or a human being. Reproduction has this dual character, that in some form it scatters small fragments of the parent far and wide as eggs that will grow up if all goes well, and that no two of the eggs will be exactly alike. Darwin himself stumbled on to this fact at the second group of islands he visited during his voyage—the Galápagos in the Pacific. Just before he had to leave, the fact dawned on him that each small island of the group, most of which were within sight of one another, not only had tortoises and finches but had tortoises and finches recognizably distinct from those on the other islands. Both the reptiles and birds had become a closed breeding stock on each island and had no truck with those across the water, the tortoises because they couldn't swim and the birds because they felt no urge to fly from their own small spot of land to another. How could these differences have come about except as a result of circumstances favoring one variety rather than another in the different places? The variability of eggs is now generally recognized as a fact of everyday existence, for obviously no two human beings look or act exactly alike unless they are identical twins, and such differences are in the main hereditary, in other words, potentially present from the beginning. And once again, returning to the question of the abandon with which nature broadcasts the seeds of the future, the more the merrier since the more eggs or seeds produced in one region or time the greater the number of variants and the greater the likelihood that some will fit the conditions awaiting them, even if the majority fail.

It works like a lottery and there is no doubt that in the literal sense the whole business is wasteful and seemingly inefficient. Chance plays an overwhelming part. It is a matter of chance whether a seed or an egg falls where conditions favor survival and growth of any sort, and it is a matter of chance whether the particular egg or seed is a little more or a little less suited to succeed than its parents would have been under these particular circumstances. Chance in the first place decided whether you yourself were to be male or female, whether you inherit this or that trait from your mother or from your father. The same holds for all other animals, and for plants as well. So that all along the line the question of chance prevails.

Look at the picture again as a whole. Death comes to all individuals and they must be replaced for a race to continue. Replacement requires an enormous number of blind shots for placement to be effective, or else some very careful aiming with bigger units, which increases the potential of the new individuals but requires a great amount of careful preparation, something that has always involved considerable evolutionary and geological time. Yet replacement is not enough. Other places may be empty and ready to serve the right kind of occupant. Or cosmic and earthly circumstances may change somewhat and the old places no longer are what they were. In either case, a new fitting is necessary and if all candidates were alike all would fail unless conditions were exactly right. Adaptation and progression in response to changing environment and colonization of new territories depend on the existence of an assortment of eggs or seeds, and the old phrase concerning the danger of putting all your eggs in one basket was apparently heard and properly considered by Mother Nature right at the start. Chance accordingly determines whether this or that egg settles where it can develop and become an active being, and chance of another kind determines whether the otherwise lucky egg is endowed with this or that particular characteristic. From the one comes the perpetual repopulation of the earth by all that live upon its surface and from the other all change in the nature of life as a whole and of its separate parts which accompanies the passage of earthly time. The question that finally arises is not so much whether the evolution of life is the result of blind chance but whether chance itself is blind. Chance is undoubtedly a great part of the operational procedure but there appears to be a system involved which somehow calls the right numbers. If the whole pattern of events which results in such as roses, bees and lyric poets make sense, and wasteful chance is a large part of it, chance itself makes sense and it is up to us to find it.

WALT

"Give me the splendid silent sun, with all his beams full-dazzling."

WHITMAN

10 : THE POTTER'S WHEEL

Life is very much like water running uphill. And water moves upward only if it is either pushed or pulled and kept more or less within a channel from which it cannot escape. So with life. Either it flows toward the future with ever-increasing complexity, drawn by a climactic fate not of our time, or it is being driven inexorably by existing forces that give it no rest, or else was set in motion long ago by creative forces—God, if you will—and has been snowballing ever since. The idea of being drawn forward by the lure of a distant goal, in other words by a built-in or superimposed purpose not unlike the carrot in front of a donkey, has apparently always had an appeal to the human mind aware of its own will and willfulness. The evidence however is otherwise.

Life, taken in its diverse whole, has an explosive quality. Cut down a forest and brush of a markedly different kind grows up at once. Exterminate wolves and other predators, and deer multiply beyond all reason. Remove the coyote and

81

prairie dogs become a pest. Let mankind commit mass suicide as it now threatens and the humanly empty earth will immediately grow rank with all that is left. Or alternatively keep up the present rate of human increase for as long as an individual redwood tree has lived and something like a million, million, million humans would exist, a mass of flesh reaching far out through the atmosphere, obviously impossible because of restricting circumstances but at least indicative of the potential power.

The restrictions imposed by space and minerals are easily seen but it is also evident that life as a whole expands to the limits of permission, pressing against the barriers at the expense of its own perishable nature. Pressing or pressed?

The answer is pressed. The essential fertilizer salts are in the shortest supply and limit the total quantity, leaving the radiant solar energy in excess. We are supplied beyond our needs by the light of the sun, and in a very real way more energy pours into the living systems than can be properly handled, or so it seems. Animals perhaps are better able to dissipate excess as some form of activity and are notable for their restlessness, males especially. All a plant can do is grow, although all manners of growth have been explored in consequence. And so in plants we find curiously complex chemical substances of great interest to a biochemist but of apparently little use to the plants producing them, as though the manufacturing process simply cannot stop where utility ends. The sun transmits abundant power for running the earthly machinery of life and it is this that is the ultimate drive continually remaking new life-forms from the debris of the old. Life was surely born of the sun, is maintained by the sun, and will continue on earth as long as the sun remains as it is. But a little more or a little less of the solar drive and the pace might well be too fast or too slow.

Yet as time goes on new models appear. If all the automobiles now in existence were the most that could be made as a result of no more lead for the making of batteries, or some such limitation, they would still wear out and the old materials could be used again. New ones would be made so long as the power was available to run the machinery, although the number of cars would not increase. But individual cars could become larger, more complicated and more streamlined if so desired, in other words could evolve, although several of the old might be needed to make one or two of the new. This of course takes for granted the machinery that produces automobiles and also how new designs are introduced, for the role of human intelligence and planning are implicit.

Put into terms of living these are among the most outstanding of all problems, for the process of designing and redesigning appears to be part of the machinery itself. At least no outside planner is in evidence. To say that God planned it all some time in the distant past, in the beginning perhaps, truly says nothing except that you cannot understand and that what cannot be understood as a natural phenomenon must have a supernatural cause. This answer simply will not do, for in effect it shuts the book in your face and suggests you had much better be picking daisies—although picking daisies is itself a subversive activity for a questing mind since the mystery and challenge of the universe lies as much in a daisy as in any other natural growth.

In this discussion of you and the universe, for discussion is all it is, I have no wish to imply in any way that we, collectively speaking, have any certain answers or that what can be discussed is necessarily well enough known and understood.

Here is a case in point. The biologist is faced, as he has from the start, with the overwhelming wonder of an invisible speck of protoplasm steadily expanding as it draws in raw material from its surroundings and finally attains relatively gigantic size and awesome complexity of structure and activity, with the wonder compounded by the fact that invisible fragments of what has thus come into being can repeat the process and reproduce exactly the same result. The phenomenon of development and the phenomenon of reproduction, using the words in their literal meaning, are partly understood, to be sure, but in so small a part that familiarity breeds not contempt but humility. If ever we gain full comprehension of these events through the power of our intellect, our victory will be mastery only in the sense in which Jacob vanquished the angel of the Lord. The challenge to understanding is greater by far than that in the life and death of a star. The human egg for instance, at about the limit of vision for the unaided eye, grows from a cell at first no more than one two-thousandths of an inch across. Yet within that cell lies all the information necessary to produce a full-grown human being capable of probing into the nature of eggs and stars and the mind itself. The outcome is staggering but so is the make-up of the cell that gives rise to it all.

Unfortunately cell structure and cell chemistry are strange to most of us and it is difficult to convey the functional perfection and actual beauty of the dynamic structure which divides a living cell into two without bringing this microscopic event actually before your eyes. Likewise the molecular structure of the chromosomes, which carry the main burden of hereditary information, that is just now becoming painfully reconstructed by biochemists, is certainly unmatched for its exquisite meaningful complexity anywhere in this solar system and possibly in the universe. The giant molecules of protein that are the main building blocks of living substance outside of the chromosomal matter are relatively simply made. Even in the case of the protein most studied, the chief component of the meat you eat and the one that contracts and relaxes in every fiber of a muscle when you move a finger or bat an eye, a leading scientist who has spent a lifetime advancing our knowledge of its action now says that the more he knows the less he understands, except that what at first appeared as a fairly straightforward problem of protein chemistry actually involves such physical considerations as electromagnetic fields, triplic excitation, and the structurization of water itself. I bring this in not to enlighten you, for the statement is far beyond my own comprehension except in the vaguest way, but to emphasize the unexpected complexity of both structure and activity of living matter. Meanwhile, with regard to the chromosomes, at least for the present, suffice it to say that each one consists of two spirally entwined molecular chains made up of units possibly equivalent to genes, thousands of units long and all different, acting in concert, and capable of serving as a blueprint or template for its own duplication. The more chemistry you know the more astounding this molecular pattern or construction becomes. Remember, too, that for most kinds of animals and plants each cell nucleus contains anywhere from a dozen to several score of uniquely different chromosomes, the number being constant for any particular kind of organism, and that when a cell divides into two each daughter cell receives the full complement. The process is precise but not easy to follow, for it is comparable to an accurate division, down to every fiber and barely discernible little hair, of a tangled ball of wool, so that in the end you have two tangled balls of wool like the first. This is in no sense a model of what goes on but it may give you some feeling of the order of difficulty and corresponding degree of success attained. And you can, of course, reach from the end into the beginning and in a manner of speaking shove the man or the bird or the flower back into the initial cell from which it grew. The potentiality of the end is in some form present at the start, expressed in interacting and interconnecting molecules and atoms of the simpler elements. We do not need to picture this primary state within the cell to appreciate its material mystery.

In spite of this involved texture of atoms in the hereditary matter, with its more or less crystalline constancy of pattern, it is not formed and fixed once and for all. The individual atoms come and go in a perpetual dance, successively replacing those in position, although the pattern persists. Energy and atoms flow continuously through the fabric, not only following but forming the pathways and strands. Yet the patterns remain, not so much despite the influx of energy and new constituents but because of it. And not merely from one moment to the next or from one cell to its immediate descendants but from parent to offspring, generation after generation throughout the centuries and millennia. A perpetual flame of a wondrous, self-duplicating and perishable kind.

Energy keeps the living flame going, energy in the first place from the sun. Energy, with matter as well of course, forces it to grow and subdivide. Energy drives it into an ever-brighter state, building molecule to molecule to the point of instability, where the construction becomes monumental and parts begin to slip. The surprising thing is that so much detail, in so dynamic a form, can be so faithfully copied or reproduced, so that identically the same rose is produced by any number of cuttings from the same stock. That copies are not always quite exact is less surprising. Yet it is these two in combination, the general exactitude and the occasional slight inexactitude, that lie at the root of change and evolution.

Exact copies are the rule, even though at first sight they may seem harder to make than inexact ones. That is a fact we have to accept, regarding it as no more and no less striking than the similarity of one crystal of salt to another. Yet the more elaborate and the more chemically active the construction becomes, the more vulnerable it is to disturbance from without and within. Chromosomes and their constituent genes, whatever these may amount to in terms of chromosomal structure, do not exist in an isolated world of their own but are subject to the influence of both chemicals and radiations entering their immediate surroundings. And between sheer instability on the one hand and radiative and chemical disturbance on the other, almost any constituent or gene along a chromosome is liable to change to something a little bit different. Such changes are mutations that will be passed on from generation to generation and are most likely to be harmful, inasmuch as an inexact copy of the original will not be as useful unless the circumstances of life have also changed. Yet harmful or not these mutations appear to be the only basis of change in general. If they are necessary evils, the evil such as it is has been turned to good, or at least into progress if that means the same thing.

Once again the whole procedure seems remarkable. Chance and waste are clearly part of the system, in fact a very large part, as though they were designed for the role they play. Certainly they are essential, as much so as paints are for a painter.

There is no need to go into all the details of the genetical situation. Large mutations from the norm are likely to be fatal. Lesser ones may be tolerated, especially since there are two of every kind of chromosome in any particular organism and only one is liable to be affected. And so with passing time the minor kinds of deviation from the party line pile up, so to speak, though they are rarely in evidence until so widespread as a result of reduplications that they begin to meet one another in matching pairs. Then the prevailing nonconformity appears in the open and we see that two living beings are rarely exactly alike. Many of the deviations or mutations appear because of the sheer instability of the hereditary molecular structure, in somewhat the same manner that uranium, the heaviest and most elaborate of the naturally occurring elements, continually breaks down with radioactive consequence. Other mutations appear as the result of bombardment by the natural radiation of the rocks forming the earth's crust, and others again from cosmic rays. In some degree even the chromosomal matter itself is radioactive, for when cosmic rays impinge on the atmosphere they convert a percentage of the nitrogen into radioactive carbon which in turn becomes incorporated together with ordinary carbon into the cells and chromosomes of plants and so finally into those of animals as well. So that a small percentage of the carbon atoms composing your own hereditary chromosomes are radioactive, progressively reverting back to nitrogen and bombarding the neighboring substance with radiative particles at the same time. No wonder there is a tendency to slip from the straight and narrow path.

Yet this is all so chancy, all of a hit-or-miss character that seems to offer no direction. If this is the wheel of chance, who spins it? Who or what makes use of such random variations or does anything else concerning them?

One answer is the environment, although this is not the whole truth. To begin with, the environment or in other words the general ircumstances of existence weed out the lame and halt, the generally unsuited, so that the stock of any particular animal or plant is virtually pruned to grow in a certain well-functioning way. In every generation the wayward branches are lopped off—even before they exist, in the case of those seeds that fall on stony ground. Once perfection or perfect fitting to particular circumstances is reached, however, further change of any sort may be more or less disastrous so long as conditions themselves remain unchanged. In such a situation the old conservative types, the old aristocracy if you like, grow better, breed better and take their place better than those that are a little bit different, and always have the advantage; and since there is never room for all, those beyond the pale are pushed to the wall continually. Some animals and some plants, such as the horseshoe crab and the ginkgo tree, have persisted unchanged for one or two hundred million years, clinging to or shifting with territories of a long-prevailing sort. In such cases variation is no more than a nuisance requiring vigilant exclusion from the common weal, although the excluder is simply the personified competition between the fit and the not quite so fit, fitness being measured in terms of efficiency in growing and reproducing. Change may therefore be frowned upon once perfect adaptation has been attained, although frowning is not always enough and evolution sometimes seems to be running with the bit in its teeth, past the winning post and past the point of no return. The giant ammonite mollusks that died out toward the end of the age of reptiles, overcumbersome and overornamented, are probably as good an example as any.

Alternatively, should the environmental circumstances change at all in any semipermanent manner, or let winds or currents carry seeds, spores, eggs or larval creatures into strange surroundings, the shoe is seen to be on the other foot. For now the old conforming aristocracy is the least likely to be best suited to the new conditions, and those that grow best and reproduce to greater extent are among the motley crowd that used to have difficulty in persisting at all. A new chance is offered and is taken, but by a new stock that has qualities of its own. And so this way and that, as the earth turns, the old life runs into fresh channels that lead to where no one knows.

Random variations and haphazard circumstances are queer partners to be in charge of such loaded freight and many have challenged their responsibility for controlling the direction. Others have dodged the issue by refusing to recognize the existence of any direction at all, assuming that what is uncontrolled must have a purely accidental outcome. Yet there is a third partner—though that is hardly the term to be used—to be considered, it is the nature of the living stuff itself. A game of chance is a good game if the possibilities of error are limited and the chances of hitting a right number are high.

All we need to assume is that living matter, like water trickling down innumerable channels of a hillside to unite as a stream with other streams and so on to the ocean, always under the compelling force of gravity, is continuously driven by solar energy and cosmic and earthly radiation into ever-increasing channels of complexity. But the possibilities are not unlimited. Just as there are only about one hundred elements all sponsored by hydrogen, so there are less than thirty kinds of the amino acid building blocks available for making the manifold patterns of protoplasmic proteins. And in the same general sense, given the complex but precise set of circumstances characteristic of a particular planet at a particular time, there are only certain ways open to the evolving life. If the number of ways were infinite nothing would arrive anywhere, but as it is, given enough tries, those that do exist will be found. The environment provides the opportunities and not too many of them, and life is driven to find them. If a boy stands near a house, throwing stones at random for long enough, sooner or later a stone will have gone through every window in sight. So it is with life that is evolving, for evolution is a natural creative process due neither to chance alone nor to design but to something venturesome that seems to belong to the universe at large, journeying like the human explorers of earlier days, venturing across the unknown world: the possibilities of discovery were manifold but not unlimited and sooner or later it was inevitable that the world would be encompassed and men would find themselves at home again. Life and mind may be equally inevitable as matter turns in upon itself under the conditions of this planet and everywhere else where comparable circumstances exist.

WALT

"Haughty this song, its words and scope,
To span vast realms of space and time,
Evolution—the cumulative—growths and generations."

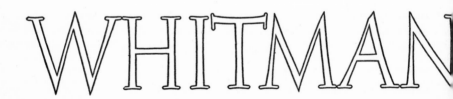

WHITMAN

11 : EMERGENT CREATION

Creation and evolution are often thought to be in opposition, as though creation does not evolve and evolution cannot create. Nothing could be further from the truth. Creative or emergent evolution is the only term that fairly fits the facts. From start to finish, from the fundamental particles of matter to the massive sculpturing mind of a Michelangelo, growth shows a surprising quality or, to put it more accurately, the quality of surprise.

In essence, it is the old familiar observation that the whole is more than the sum of its parts, which is so clearly true for almost everything you can see or think of that we would be astonished if it were otherwise. You see it in reverse when an old house is being torn down to become merely a pile of bricks and rubble—all the extra meaning dissolves before your eyes. In the same way a wilted flower or a stricken bird is pitiful, while a child dead is virtually unbelievable. The loss is all too evident. Yet this is a backward point of view.

93

To see nature in its real perspective you need to look from the beginning forward into time, from the small to the large, and from the simple to the complex. For out of unions and expansions new properties and phenomena emerge that have all the appearance of novelty—that is, could not have been forecast from knowledge of the separate components. Nothing that chemists and physicists know about the properties of hydrogen and oxygen either as elements or as gases would have led them to suspect the unique qualities of water or the symmetries of snow and frost crystals. When carbon is added to the same two elements, a whole new chemical universe arises, the study of which is now a science in itself, including substances ranging from sweet sugars to high-octane gasoline and the cream in your coffee; and once again we can comprehend the relationship of the whole to its parts in each instance only by virtue of hindsight. At each new level a new vista opens which cannot be anticipated.

All along the line, through the ascending series of elements from hydrogen to iron and on to radioactive uranium, throughout the molecular world of chemists from water and salts to the contractile fibers of a muscle, and in the realm of life from microbes to humming birds and human beings, as small units are joined together or as one item is added to another, the whole pattern changes as though you had shifted a kaleidoscope. With every new arrangement new qualities appear which may transform the old completely. Nothing so typifies the basic stuff of the universe as this truly creative process and the more you examine it the more awe inspiring it becomes.

At the surface of this planet, the sun's radiation continuously forces matter out of its natural inertia. The air is kept in turbulent motion, water is drawn up from the seas and the moist land so that rain falls and eroding water runs richly laden back to the sea; green vegetation everywhere is driven to produce increasingly complex substances, with increasing storage of energy, and animal life in turn is thereby driven to transcend itself. From level to level the sun-driven flood of creation mounts up: the particles, whatever they really are, combine as atoms, the atoms as molecules, molecules as half-alive viruses, and so linkage by linkage to cells and on to the multicellular flowers, jellyfish and tigers with all their fearful symmetry. In short, energy transforms to matter, matter to life, and life to mind and loveliness.

Such is the general trend produced by the interaction of the sun and the earth. Yet within this broad direction, the forms of growth and creative beauty are restricted, much as the sprouting of weeds in a newly plowed field is determined by the kinds of seeds that have lain fallow in the soil. Herein lies the general directiveness and apparent purposefulness of evolution. Solar and other cosmic radiation drives life along some general course to the extent of keeping it in motion, like a goad to an ox.

The peculiarities of the earth as a planet—in other words, the special nature of the earthly environment—make certain things or events possible and not others. While the particular kind or kinds of living substance characteristic of the earth is also limited in what it can or cannot do by its own nature, had it originally been a little different in one way or another, the more prominent forms of life would have been different, too, although in much more apparent ways. The protoplasm which did come into existence here in the early days of the planet obviously has had a manifold capacity for evolving into very diverse kinds of animals and plants, yet at all times that capacity has been far from infinite. Consequently we see much the same sort of biological inventions cropping up again and again throughout the plant and animal kingdom, especially in the latter where evolution has been more complex and venturesome.

It is as though the sun said to life: "Get up and get going." And the cosmos said: "You can go anywhere you like so long as you don't leave the changing earth." And life replied: "But I can only move eastward for I must meet the rising sun." So every morning we rise and shine in a different place in space and time and in a different state of being. And every day life evolves a little, but in a manner and in a general direction inborn and imposed almost from the start. Such are the purposiveness and design in evolution, which is accordingly no seeking of a distant goal somewhere in the future, as many men including a few biologists have thought, but a journey in a certain direction away from the starting place, with no goal beckoning but only an adventure into uncharted seas, with many landfalls already made and many more to come, though never the final discovery that ends the voyage. For then all would be over and without life even the past might be dead.

In spite of this channeling of life's advance the pageant of evolution as seen from our present eminence in time is magnificent in its diversity, in its interrelatedness and in its progressive embellishment of the planetary surface through the course of ages. At all times each local advance has had repercussions throughout the whole, and with every change more opportunity has appeared for some kinds of life and less for others, whether the changes have been in circumstances or in living things themselves. And every new living discovery has remained a burden as well as an inspiration to future life, just as our own discovery of atomic energy will remain to plague us as well as to revolutionize our ways of living. We reach for the future but contend with the past, and the greater and richer the past the more there is to contend with. And still it is the past that gives us such direction as we have, like the wake of a ship in a trackless ocean.

The primary diversity, so far as it concerns our present and familiar world, occurred when plants became plants in the chlorophyll way, particularly when chlorophyll became packaged in plastids within the cells. From that time on, far away in the dim Pre-Cambrian era, plant life has gone one way, set in its course by its own discovery, and animal life in a sense leapfrogged over the plants to a higher plane, or at least took a short cut to a more active existence. Yet far back in the beginning, during the time all organisms were but microscopic single cells living their individual lives, before even the splitting into plant and animal stocks took place, the shape of the future was sketched out in certain very important ways. With the chemistry of living substance already well developed, even to the universal presence of typical digestive enzymes and a cellular respiratory pigment, these primitive forms of life had already achieved the amazing and still more or less mysterious machinery for dividing into two that is shared by the growing tissues of oaks and elephants alike; and in addition the fundamental nature and purpose of sex was well established. No wonder the facts of life are often taught to children in terms of pollination of flowers by bees, to the utter confusion of all concerned.

From single cells to many cells intimately united, the step was obvious, both among the green ones and the rest, and from then onward the expanding upward path to the giants was open.

To a very great extent evolution has been an unavoidable process of adjustment to the needs and complications involving in sheer increasing size, and an exploitation of the new qualities and properties exhibited by large masses of living substance which were impossible to express on a smaller scale. The analogy with a brick building is useful once more. However you may cut or shape a single brick, your scope is extremely limited and you cannot make a house out of it even for a mouse. With a score or so your freedom begins, though only in a suggestive way. When bricks are available by the billion there is almost no end to the sort of construction you can make, although at all stages, whatever it is, you are restricted by the nature of the bricks. Stones of varying size and shape may increase your range and your problems as well, although in the absence of steel and concrete, should you wish to build something large and tall to hold a thousand persons in religious ceremony, you will tend to build a cathedral whether you have had it in mind or not. And the larger it is the more cathedral-like the building will be, if it is to stand up securely, though the forms of growth may at last take on a vitality of their own. Thus Persian mosques, Flemish cathedrals and Buddhist temples have a family resemblance that would strike a visitor from Mars at once, despite great superficial distinctions.

The situation is similar for living organisms. Cells, however peculiar or intricate any particular kinds may be, remain minute, varying in size only within a certain microscopic range. If they grow beyond that size, they divide to form more cells but not larger cells, each small cell continuing to need maintenance in the accustomed manner. Such is the basis of growth and inasmuch as growth is a natural property of living matter, there is a general tendency for all living things that consist of many cells to grow larger as they grow older. Large size, of course, can become an encumbrance and there are many advantages in not being too big. On the other hand, while large size itself creates all manner of structural and maintenance problems, the larger animals and plants are relatively immune from destruction by smaller animals or by the elements of wind and water.

One of the most impressive features of the history of life as recorded in fossils is the progressive evolution of large kinds from smaller kinds. The tendency to grow larger with time, in part, perhaps, as an evolutionary analogy with having to keep up with the Joneses, is as typical of evolution as it is of individuals, although limits are set in every instance. Increase in size undoubtedly brings advantages. It inevitably brings problems. And it may bring surprises. Some examples are helpful here.

We start with the assumption, though recognition is better, that whatever changes in size or shape a creature may undergo either as an individual or as a race, it must maintain an overall efficiency. In more fundamental terms, each constituent cell of the body must be kept in a state of well-being, the process of digestion must keep up with the demands of the tissues no matter how massive they become, the heart must pump not merely as well as before but must propel greater and greater quantities of blood the larger the animal becomes. A falling off in efficiency at any point cancels out any advantage of large size that might have been gained. Animals especially have had to make continual adjustments to compensate for every outward change in form or dimensions.

The long neck of the giraffe has been a topic for speculation for over a century. One popular interpretation is that the neck grew long to enable the giraffe to feed on the foliage of treetops. The more likely explanation is very different. In the first place, giraffes are browsing animals of grasslands infested by lions and other large cats, and like all such creatures those who can successfully run away live to feed and breed another day. So the legs of giraffes have grown longer with the passing of many generations, the longer-legged individuals surviving by virtue of greater speed and also perhaps because their bodies are higher off the ground for a cat to reach. Everything favors the long legs. On the other hand, long legs alone are a liability for, while they spell safety, the ground where water and grass lie is still at the level of the feet. So as legs grew long during giraffe evolution, the neck grew long accordingly, simply because at all times the creatures needed to drink and crop and to do so without kneeling down. One extension was a condition for the other. At the same time, the long neck enabled its owner to feed on foliage beyond the reach of its shorter-necked ancestors and to see the approach of enemies from a greater distance. These are the dividends and not the capital itself.

Circumstances shape an organism. Trees are trees not because they are necessarily more closely related to one another than to other plants that are far from being tree-like but because they are plants grown large, on land, in close proximity to one another. Many kinds of plants have become tree-like under such conditions. Unless there is elbow room, the only way a plant can grow is up, and in any case when too much light is cut off by other vegetation growing alongside there is a race to reach the upper canopy of the forest where light is adequate and perhaps abundant. Those that grow fast and tall with spreading green growth at the top can keep their metabolic factories going and can mature and set their seed, but only if more or less hardwood is laid down to form an ever-widening trunk as support for the upper growth and transportation of sap. And such a structure needs spreading buttressing roots that can also probe deep or wide for water. Trees of one kind or another, from the tree ferns of coal-forest age to more recent maples and mimosas, have been inevitable creations, once plants began to grow on land, supporting their own weight, and close together.

And so in the sea. To move fast through water, which is many times as dense as air, considerable power is required and as little resistance as possible. The shape and fins of a fish are characteristics imposed on any mass of muscle and nerve that must move with stability rapidly through a liquid medium. The greater the muscle the greater the power, and the better the body is streamlined the less work there is to be done. Between the two a flexible tapering form emerges which is fitting for its purpose. Fish have it, particularly those that swim fastest and farthest, and they have given the shape its name, which is also fitting since fish are the oldest stock of this kind. The need to conform, however, is shown by other creatures that have taken to a life in the oceans at later times. During the age of reptiles, great lizards returned to the sea on more than one occasion to feed on fish and mollusks, and became as fish-like in form as any fish, though they remained air-breathing reptiles inside their skin. At a later time both birds and mammals have again become essentially marine, such as penguins and auks and porpoises and whales—in each case acquiring the form and function of a fish as much as possible, though more successfully in the mammal than in the bird. In other words, to live like a fish you must look like a fish, no matter what your real nature may be. You see the same compulsion in the shape of a submarine. By the same token, if you want to fly you must have wings—a truism maybe, but only as a result of overfamiliarity—and the wings may be the arms of a bird, the hands of a bat or of the extinct reptilian pterodactyls, or growths from a butterfly's back, placed like those of an angel.

Gravity and growth and the need for light and water evoked the tree; the need to move fast and the resistance to liquid molded the form of a fish; and the insubstantiality of air demanded wings for any that would leave the ground. These are all fairly obvious associations. There are others of greater import.

Living matter is sensitive to most of the forces of the universe, though not all, for magnetic force appears not to affect us and radio waves ignore us, but even plants are subject to light and gravity. Animals are much more so and in great part their very nature lies in this sensitivity and their capacity to respond. Yet it all goes back to free-living, single-celled organisms, to those in fact which cannot be completely classified either as animal or plant but seem to incline both ways at once. Protoplasm, speaking at once of virtually all kinds of living cells or tissues, plant or animal or in between, is generally irritable, using this term in its more precise meaning; that is, responsive to all that lies without—nervous even without nerves, light-sensitive without eyes, contractile without muscle, and so on. When such as these are recognizable in even the smallest of living things, leaving bacteria and viruses apart, we should not be surprised to find in larger creatures consisting of billions of cells that specialization takes place among the various units and that some groups of cells, for instance, are set aside especially for the reception of light. Eyes of many types, built on various plans and ranging from mere light-sensitive pigment spots to direction-finding eyes and image-forming eyes are seen scattered through the animal kingdom, all of them evolutionary exploitations or developments of the basic sensitivity of protoplasm itself to light. It is notable too that the sensitivity is to the light spectrum as received through a shallow layer of water, which cuts out almost all the ultraviolet and the infrared. This is the light to which we and the rest were originally accustomed. As human beings with uncomfortably inquiring minds we need artificial aids to see beyond it at either end.

There are however one or two exceptions to prove the rule: bees see much farther into the ultraviolet than we do, and owls see heat rays in the dark which we do not! Yet even image-forming eyes have come into existence at least several times, starting practically from scratch, and so has color vision. The mosaic eyes of dragon flies and crabs are of a pattern fundamentally different from those of fish and men, but they form images and are extremely efficient at detecting and measuring movement. We and our backboned relatives have camera eyes, of which the modern camera is essentially a copy. Taken alone such an eye is a marvelous evolutionary invention, but it appears more so when we realize that it has happened twice, in all its intricacy, present not only as part of the vertebrate animal's equipment but of the giant mollusks such as the squid and octopus as well. The two models are not exactly alike and they are produced in different ways, as might be expected in two such mutually alien groups, but the general similarity is so remarkable and the complexity in each case so great that many scientists, and nonscientists, have been much troubled to account for it. If you should discover a lobster making and operating an electronic computer, your problem and astonishment would be much the same. What is shown, I believe, is that whether animal protoplasm has acquired a molluscan or a vertebrate garb, its responsiveness to light leads inevitably to the construction of eyes of one sort or another so long as their value is great in terms of survival of their owners and if millions of generations have been available for their perfection; for these are sense organs that came into being long,

long ago and the time available for their formation may well have been many hundred millions of years, not necessarily so but time was there for the taking.

The evolving animal life of those ancient days responded in a constructive way not only to light but to gravity, contact and the chemistry of the environment, especially in the more animated or active groups. Eyes, gravity-sensitive organs, tactile senses, organs for detecting the nature and source of unusual chemicals in the surrounding water came into existence in various forms in the different stocks, but in every case all connecting with nerve cells and fibers. The larger and more diverse the sense organs, the larger and more complex the nerve mass necessary for receiving their stimuli and translating the information into meaningful activity. In other words, general sensitivity led to special sense organs and they in turn, simply through common association at a single switchboard at the front end of the organism, brought brains into being. Sensation, awareness, and related action are the natural outcome of the primary properties of primitive protoplasm, but as animal organisms have grown in size during evolutionary time, sense organs and brains have also grown and with their growth new phenomena emerge. Just as matter by growing together in certain ways becomes alive, so living substance in turn acquires awareness as it grows. You can see this happen before your eyes every time an egg develops.

Evolution is a creative process. That is a conclusion based on the study of fossils in the successive layers of rock and on the study of living things as they are. The time scale is too vast and the rate of change too slow, however, for the process to be seen directly. It is different with a developing egg or seed. No room for argument exists although it has not always been so. Until about a century ago the inadequacy of microscopes permitted wild imaginings of what lay beyond the limits of vision; and reproductive cells, human in particular, were thought to contain infinitely compact folded replicas of the creature-to-be, and development was considered as essentially an expansion of a preformed individual much as you see in the unfolding of a flower in the last phase of its growth. Now we know better. The remarkable thing about an egg, whether fertilized or not, is the absence of all that is to come. Potentially everything is there, certainly, or else nothing would emerge, but actually very little is present to begin with that is not in most cells that are not overspecialized. Development is not an unfolding, it is creation in the most real sense of that word. In many ways, except for the safety and normality of the procedure, it is a pity that all that is most eventful in human development takes place out of sight, for here, as in other cases, out of sight means out of mind. Yet a frog's egg can show you the same sort of emergent creative process. Hour by hour the originally single cell which was the egg divides into progressively more and smaller cells. After a day or so there is a primitive gut and a blueprint of the brain, and a symmetry you can recognize as that of the tadpole and frog-to-be. A day or two later the now-enclosed brain has sent out a pair of outgrowths to the side which become the retinas of the eyes, and pockets grow in from the skin to meet them and form their lens. Gradually but inexorably the whole elaborate structure of the body comes into being, vaguely at first but with ever-increasing detail until, at the end of a week, everything essential to an actively swimming backboned animal is present, none of which was evident at the start. If eyes and ears and brain and heart formed from the seemingly structureless basic living substance is not a case of creation, nothing is. It takes time, to be sure, and is not instantaneous and is not a production of something from nothing. But beyond all cavil, with the expansion of a seed of life, whether an egg, a spore, or an actual seed, new structure, new properties and new functions steadily emerge—leading to senses and minds, to flowers, to lovely form and to sinister intent, to all the richness of the living world. None of it is perpetuated as such and everything is continually re-created from more or less invariable starting points—every blossom is a new blossom, every person a new person, who has come into existence in a manner that so far defies understanding, though we can see it happen. If our own sense of time were different or if the events or processes of development could be accelerated a hundred times, we would appreciate the phenomenon as a creative motion. Since it is usually too slow to catch the eye as activity or movement we generally overlook it and an intellectual effort is required to sense it. Our common unawareness however is irrelevant. The reality is there—creative development in every individual life and creative evolution through the course of ages.

"Then last of all, caught from these shores, this hill
    Of you O tides, the mystic human meaning:
    Only by law of you, your swell and ebb, enclosing me the same,
    The brain that shapes, the voice that chants this song."

12 : BRAINS AND SENSES

Life is vital, animals are animated and some but by no means all are aware of the world around them. Some creatures such as jellyfish have nervous systems but have no brains. Others have brains and sense organs but apparently little awareness. A few kinds have awareness raised to a high pitch, with intelligence to match. Human beings, chimpanzees and dogs exhibit various degrees of self-consciousness. Humans alone seem to be aware of their self-consciousness. The ascending scale is clear enough and in a general way presents the order of appearance upon the earth through the course of time.

We know that we ourselves have minds and we regard ourselves as intelligent and even wise, and we recognize at least a degree of intelligence in our mammalian pets and nearest relatives. What of the rest? To what extent are consciousness, awareness and intelligence emergent properties of life in general, as distinct from a freakish break-through in one particular group? Are we with our sensitivity to situations a biological accident of no more real significance than a toadstool or any other living production? This is a crucial question for although life in general may be the most significant expression of a planet we can only regard awareness and intelligence as being of greater import if they in turn are as inevitable as life itself, given suitable circumstances.

To answer the question requires that we look briefly at the animal kingdom as a whole to see to what extent the various creatures that do show these qualities are related to one another. If, for instance, all such comprise a single closely knit group then we have but a single, though diversified, event of its kind, and a single event of any kind may always be an exception to a rule. On the other hand, if the same qualities crop up in basically unrelated stocks they can be considered to be qualities latent in living substance as such, which is what we find.

Three groups of animals are dominant at present and have been since time out of mind—the backboned kind, to which we belong; the insects; and the giant mollusks of the sea now represented mainly by the octopus and squid. Each group could put forward a good claim to priority if pressed. The mollusks were marine giants with enormous camera eyes and a respectable brain before there was ever a fish in the ocean, descended from slug-like animals of far more ancient seas; insects are not so antique but in numbers and kinds outstrip all the rest of the living world together, taking their own origin from worm-like creatures among the earliest green cover of the land; backboned forms, leading to fishes and birds and all the four-footed animals on earth, grew from nearly blind creatures swimming in the oldest rivers. Somewhere in the very far distant past all three groups would find a common relationship, but so far back that we can well forget it. The important point now is that each of the three lines have evolved in its own way from virtually brainless and ill-equipped ancestors and each has produced elaborate sense organs and a brain worthy of the name. In each case as the stock has evolved, sense organs relating the organism to light, to gravity, to external contacts and to the chemicals in the surroundings have come into being, and in each case a brain has grown as a clearing and storing house for impressions received. The idea is the same though the patterns are different. The conclusion is clear. Independently in three widely different cases of animal evolution, sense organs, brains, awareness and at least a degree of intelligence have emerged from living tissue that was little more than sensitive and irritable. This being so, it becomes worth our while to examine the senses and minds of these three types of torchbearers.

The mollusk comes first, not only because it was first in time but because it remains in the primeval saltwater environment whereas the others have become essentially what they are in other regions. Primitively mollusks were sluggish creatures of the sea floor, probably with light-sensitive but not image-forming eyes, carrying comparatively heavy armor in the shape of a shell. Gravity raised no problem since they rested heavily on the ground. From such as these have come the squids, cuttlefish and octopus of the present, marine creatures generally ignored since they are rarely caught and do not contribute to human welfare, although by direct evidence we know that squids have bodies at least thirty feet long, with tentacles to match, equipped with eyes a foot in diameter, and that in the deep seas, where they feed on fish and where great sperm whales feed on them, they undoubtedly grow to two or three times the size. And they are fast swimmers, shaped like rockets for shooting backward. The octopus is a shallow-water relative with a flexible body for squeezing in and out of rocky crevices and is much more readily confined in an aquarium where its activities can be studied.

In the first place the octopus, especially if it is a female, builds a nest or home in a corner out of stones and shells—a lair, if you prefer; and it can be taught to come out for food, to associate food with white plates even though the food is lacking, to disregard such plates if they also convey electric shocks, and so on. In other words, the creature is not only aware of its surroundings and what is going on but is most decidedly able to learn and to learn from experience. It has intelligence. The order of intelligence may not be high but that is beside the point. What is significant is that here, in a group of animals as remote from our own vertebrate stock as it is possible to find, intelligence recognizably similar in kind to our own, if not in degree, has come independently into being. Moreover, the octopus not only possesses memory, that is, some record of past events, but investigation has shown in what part of its brain the memory is mainly stored. A general theory or hypothesis concerning how intelligence comes into existence has been based on studies of this particular animal.

It is a matter of senses and nerve centers. Wherever sense organs are to be found, among animals in general, from worms up, a localized center of nerve cells forms at least a semblance of a brain associated with them and the pattern of the brain reflects the nature of the senses. If sense organs such as eyes are large, corresponding parts of the brain are large, since there must be a matching of brain cells to the number of retinal cells. In the case of the octopus, there is a pair of large camera eyes comparable to our own, although they are a purely molluscan creation, with large optic lobes in the brain which lies between—sight is certainly a dominant sense. But there is more. Organs of balance, gravity-sensitive, are even within the central brain itself. Organs of chemical sense lie in the gill chambers and elsewhere and have their own representation in the brain. Taste organs lie in the mouth. Yet, much more than these, a sense of touch extends in highly developed fashion over the surface and suckers of the eight long arms, apart from the rest of the body. All of the senses—except hearing and perhaps pain—that we possess, the octopus appears to have, too, and this seems to be the secret. The collection of sense organs in a way creates a central brain for their mediation or else they would be useless. The one goes with the other and there is little doubt that they have evolved together. Intelligence arises as the result of continual excitation and in the octopus one or more or even all of the various sense organs are firing impulses into the brain at any one time, keeping the electrical waves in constant motion. You can see how it is yourself. When you go to bed and close your eyes, stop talking or otherwise disturbing yourself, and switch off your ears, you fall asleep. Your brain lacks sensory stimulus enough to keep awake and you become barely conscious and certainly unintelligent.

So much for a mollusk! What about insects? There is little doubt that most insects conduct their affairs instinctively with little awareness and no intelligence, but there are exceptions; bees are possibly the most outstanding. In any case, all that we are looking for is a clear example of mental activity in a group of animals that cannot be significantly related to either mollusks or men. Insects are such a group and bees, to put it mildly, are astounding, especially in view of their size. A bee is small and the brain residing within its head is smaller still; yet proportionately the brain is impressive and it connects with relatively large eyes, image-forming but not camera-type, with very extensively distributed organs for touch, with organs for taste and, far from least, with highly developed organs for smell. The details are not important. What is significant is that the same general set-up is here as exists in the octopus— a battery of different sense organs all firing into a common center or brain. If one kind is quiet the rest are not, and so long as temperatures are high enough a bee appears to be conscious and aware of its surroundings, even in the dark. The sensory equipment is there, the brain is there, though small, and the performance is remarkable although much of it is probably not intelligent. Again very briefly, a foraging bee flies from the hive, discovers and feeds on a new crop of flowers and takes a beeline back to the hive in spite of having flown outward along an erratic course. Within the hive it dances, with its fellows following behind, and in so doing, in the dark and on a vertical surface, somehow communicates the direction, the distance and the aroma of the flowers it had fed upon, all of which may be instinctive or automatic without implying the need or existence of intelligence, marvellous though it be. Yet worker bees within the hive are now known to wander around and finish up any one of a number of unfinished projects left by other bees, which indicates appraisal of a situation and adjustment of activity to fit the circumstances. This is behavior that has all the earmarks of intelligence rather than the rigid responses of instinct. The bee has the equipment and the central brain, but as a member of a large and complex hive society it is forced into constant action, its senses are continually excited, and so, apparently, intelligence and memory have come to be. How much memory and how much intelligence is beside the point—that they have arisen at all, independently of other sections of the animal kingdom, is the significant event.

And so with the backboned creatures as a whole. It is unimportant whether we can demonstrate intelligence in fish, reptiles or birds since we have no doubt concerning its presence in mammals, quite apart from ourselves. Fish can, however, be taught to discriminate and to respond to meaningful signals; the memory of birds on returning migrations is apparently very great indeed. In warm-blooded mammals intelligence at least of a low level is widespread and well known, and again depends on the existence of a variety of sense organs communicating with the brain as a common center—with stimuli pouring in not only as before through eyes, organs of smell and taste, and diffusely scattered terminals for several kinds of touch, but through ears as well. A state of cerebral wakefulness or consciousness is maintained most of the time by continual excitation of the brain. You see it in a dog and you feel it in yourself.

Look for a moment at the over-all picture. The surface of any naked cell is responsive to light, to contacts and to almost any kind of chemical reaching it. From such a general sensitivity we can trace the evolution of special organs concerned with this or that particular reception, so that eyes of various types and diverse organs relating to smell and taste and touch appear in almost every active group independently within the animal kingdom. Central clearing houses of nerve cells go hand in hand with the sense organs, for neither can work without the other, and brains of a sort are the natural outcome. This seems to be the general direction of evolving animal life no matter from where we start among the primitive stocks. Viewed with detachment, what we are seeing is just a general responsiveness of living matter to all the more changeable forces of the cosmos, from stellar radiation to physical and chemical impacts, and the gradual or progressive concentration of sensitivity and response within a special region we call a brain. Above all, perhaps, we should see this whole event as a reaction between matter which is alive and the manifold forces which lie outside it. And following this point of view through, we see awareness, consciousness, and intelligence itself, emerging as properties of this continuing reaction. This manner of speaking may seem a little farfetched. It is not. It is merely an effort to withdraw far enough from the immediate present and all the details of our own earthly existence and of our animal and vegetable companions in order to sense even vaguely what is actually going on. The difficulty is great and is comparable to that of seeing the historical significance of the political and economic events taking place at the present time, in which we ourselves are involved; or of a psychotic individual attempting to diagnose his own peculiar state of mind, although such a person can call in a psychiatrist to do the job for him while we cannot.

On this scale of evolutionary achievement and discovery, where do we as humans find our own place? If senses, consciousness and elementary intelligence are general emergent phenomena in three separate sections of the animal kingdom, are we as human beings distinctively different in kind from those other mammals that show intelligence in some degree? I believe that we are. I think that a line can be drawn at the mental level between the mind of man and the mind of an ape, let alone that of any less related creature, a line that is like the wall separating the world at large from the confines of a prison. We possess essentially the same kind of brain as apes and monkeys but we do have more of it and somehow connected with this increase our distinction comes. At the same time, when you think of the brain of a bee and how much it can do with so little, it seems that we ought to function better than we do when we have so much.

It is puzzling, too, that there is so little to be seen in the brain of an ape that suggests it could not perform the same sort of mental feats as our own. Wherein lies the difference and what does it mean? Actually, I suppose, the ape brain and ape behavior are so close to the threshold of freedom and are so similar to what the human was a second ago in geological time that we should see ourselves even now as standing but just outside the walls of confinement—not as the experienced explorers of the cosmos but as newly freed prisoners blinking in the sunlight.

However this may be and whatever semblance we may discover in the fundamental procedures of problem-solving by apes and men, the mental jump from the one to the other is of as great an order of magnitude as that which separates primitive sensory awareness from simple intelligent action. The break-through has actually taken time enough if we include the various subhuman and late anthropoid steps—several million years at least—and it is only in relation to the whole period of evolutionary time that it appears short. All manner of agents appear to have come together to bring about the result: the absolute increase in brain size, the relative increase of fore brain regions, the acquisition of speech and all that this makes possible concerning communication and verbal memory of spoken thought, the prolongation of the life span and especially the prolongation of the impressionable and adaptable phases of childhood and adolescence, and not least the formation of family or tribal societies in which mutual stimulation and excitation are constantly present. This is all a long and complex story that has been told at length elsewhere. In the present setting the striking thing is that there has clearly been a great intensification of all the factors that we have seen to be responsible for the initial emergence of conscious intelligent behavior. If the brains of bees and octopuses are what they are because of almost unceasing stimulation, if the brains and activities of apes and monkeys are what they are because lifting high off the ground in tropical forests has added sensory excitement and athletic challenge to an already potent mammalian brain, it is not surprising that the general circumstances of prehuman life, embracing as they did a descent from the trees and a rigorous exposure to nearly a million years of a fluctuating ice age, should culminate in an entirely new level of attainment. It is as though you had a variety of metals in a furnace and suddenly raised the temperature to their point of fusion—the resulting alloy has qualities of its own.

Obviously this complex event has occurred but once or else we would be contending for mastery of the earth with other creatures of a caliber similar to our own. Yet it is conceivable that the same sort of break-through at the mental level might take place a number of times if life as a whole persists long enough and if those who have succeeded first do not scuttle the ship for those who might otherwise have made the venture later. The fact is, however, that we who call ourselves human are the first and possibly the last to reach this platform of emergence on this planet, and that the only hope of pushing further in this direction lies with us.

We have truly broken through the barriers to a new level; that seems certain, although the analogy is not the best. Perhaps no analogy is now adequate to illustrate the reality. The main thing is that there has been increase in three dimensions together, counting space as one. The material basis of the mind, the brain itself, compared with that of the nearly human ape, has increased twofold in both bulk and fine complexity; the duration of its growth and maturing has increased by much more than twofold; and the day by day excitation also has markedly increased.

The outcome is a new level and scale of perception, of general awareness; of the storage of the past in the form of memory relating to sight, sound and motion; and a sense of future time as well as time past. This is not the place for an exposition of these various qualities—in many ways we are all too conscious of them; conscious of our own tensions and emotional turmoils; conscious of human history and the precarious nature of our future; and conscious of our accomplishments in science, arts and industry; in fact, conscious that we are far brighter than we are wise. The sense of time, the sense of beauty, the intellectual reach into matter and through the universe, and the spiritual reach for the meaning behind it all—the search for God—all these are new at least on earth. There is a new glory here but it is freshly undeveloped and holds a still greater promise.

Yet the past also remains. As human beings we are aware of all that is new in this exciting adventure of which we are individually a part, but we carry our past with us in many ways. The emotional and irrational surgings of our anthropoid ancestry remain to plague us in both personal and international relations; we are more masters of our enviroment than of ourselves. At the same time it is the particular form of the prehuman past that has given us much of what we most cherish. Our sense of color almost certainly came from living in the sunlit and colorful world of the treetops, for all ground-living mammals are without it; and for the same reason smell has little meaning to us though it dominates those who stayed down below. Tree-life demanded binocular vision with eyes that move in conjunction, which gives us a sense of space and distance that is virtually ours alone, and also the ability to converge all sight for purposive action—leading to intentions to reach the moon and Mars and by a queer sort of inward shift to an intention to control the direction of our own future evolution. All that we are and all that we are not are legacies from a past that has been peculiar, fantastic and unique. Circumstances have molded us and the creation that has now emerged is trying to take command. And if we say it is almost within our grasp, figuratively speaking, it is because circumstances demanded hands in place of feet! The progress of life is devious, traveling in erratic and surprising ways to reach unexpected ends, with each end serving at least potentially as a new beginning. And so we stand, at the end of the line and at the start of the next.

WALT

"Would you sound below the restless ocean of the entire world?
Would you know the dissatisfaction? the urge and spur of every
life?
The something never still'd—never entirely gone? the invisible
need of every seed?"

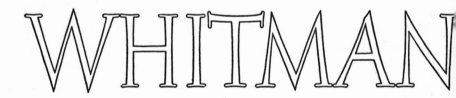

WHITMAN

13 : THE LIMITS OF THE EARTH

The film of life covering the earth's surface may be thin; nevertheless it possesses a third dimension although its distribution is uneven and circumstances cause it to grow or dwindle. On the land it is seen in its greatest richness and diversity on the lowlands of the warmer regions; and in colorful variety in warm shallow seas and in abundance, though less colorful, in the subpolar oceans. There is a lively sort of life in lakes and rivers and streams. The soil contains a multitude of forms, from earthworms and cutworms to the myriad microscopic organisms that constitute a world to themselves. Vegetation and animal life of some sort extend high up on mountainsides and northward to the barren grounds. Even the air some thousand feet up carries a diversity of dormant spores, while in the deep oceanic abyss strange creatures of various kinds drift or swim or crawl about five miles beneath the surface. A few peculiar types live out their lives in the streams within terrestrial caverns and some manage to survive in hot sulphur

123

springs at temperatures close to the boiling point. Wherever there is water, on this planet, there is life, too, and often where no water has been seen for many a year, life waits in dried but potent expectancy.

Where do the limits lie? Where are circumstances the best? Which is the natural homestead of life? How have the restless wanderers succeeded in colonizing other regions? Questions such as these crop up as soon as we think of life in particular rather than as a whole. The variety of living things is staggering, and the simple task of classifying and cataloguing them is monumental and far from finished. The world they live in is itself so variable, with every latitude and longitude and horizontal level setting conditions different from the rest. To say that variety is the spice of life is true enough, though it is an understatement and you could say it is the essence of life and be closer to the truth.

Yet variety is not infinite, either in the permutations of living organisms or in the range of environmental conditions that tolerate their existence. The fundamental limitation is water. Life must be liquid to be lively, and so can function only between the temperature of freezing and boiling, at least so far as the living matter itself is concerned. Even that narrow range represents the whole range for all life. A particular kind, whether animal or plant, is its natural unspoiled self only within a portion of it. Living tissues jellify usually well above the freezing point, not necessarily killed but no longer, for the time being at least, performing any living action; higher up the scale the same tissues coagulate, as irreversibly as an egg that has been boiled, but at temperatures you would find comfortable to bathe in. For most sea creatures and many others, the total range is merely a small part of the whole, way down in the water realm. Living things on land as a rule can put up with higher temperatures, but even the desert lizards die in the sun in a very short while and make use of what shade they can find. In spite of the fact that human beings can live more or less successfully all the way from the high tropics to the polar ice, they enter a chill coma if the body temperature drops just a few degrees, and expire with a fever if it rises even as high as a sparrow's. The level that human tissues can tolerate is high, but the range is narrow, indeed.

Other than birds and mammals, however, all living things are at the mercy of the temperature of their surroundings, caught within narrow limits of heat and cold even in terms of liquidity. The range itself may be higher or lower on the watery scale but wherever it happens to be it remains small in scope. And this general situation is fraught with significance, if only we can find the meaning, and raises a question as profound as any that have yet been posed to human thought. It concerns the fitting of the earth to the special nature of living matter, which is like putting the cart before the horse.

This is the way of it: Simply as a form of matter all living substance is immensely complex, how much so we are only now beginning to suspect, and at the same time it is in a dynamic condition resembling a state of equilibrium. Consequently the basic requirement for its healthy existence is stability or as constant an external environment as possible. Any cosmic draught would blow out the living flame as quickly as your breath could extinguish a candle's. A wildly fluctuating temperature would give simple forms of life little chance to survive and would have made their creation impossible, for nothing so delicately complicated could have been built unless evolutionary patience was permitted to play its game undisturbed for a period longer than we can imagine. The marvel is that such wondrous stuff can exist at all, not that it needs so much nurture and security. This being so, it should not come as a surprise that the earth meets the requirements so perfectly. Had it been otherwise life may well have not come into being. In other words, we find life and ideal circumstances together or not at all. And still the circumstances cannot be taken for granted.

Look for a moment at the earth as a whole. The planet is so placed relative to the sun that the seas, land surface and atmosphere are warmed at the equator but cooled at the poles which are several thousand miles farther away from the source of heat. The result is a continuous flow of cold air and water from polar regions toward the equator and a corresponding flow of warmer air and water toward the poles, maintaining between them a circulation and a remarkably constant temperature at any given latitude. Moreover, ice floats on water, the only solid to float in its own liquid, and consequently the polar oceans have never been in any danger of freezing all the way to the bottom. Added to the polar-equatorial mixing is an averaging of another kind, the spinning of the planet around its own axis, which keeps the side exposed to the sun from becoming overheated and prevents the dark side from getting too cold. The temperature is kept more or less even by the continuous spin. With a slower rate of rotation the difference between day and night would be greater and if there was no rotation at all the sunny side would be far too hot and the dark side far too cold for any sort of life to survive in active form. If placement and spin are accidents, then life must be accidental. If life is not accidental, although dependent upon chance—there is a distinction—the planetary spacing and spinning must have their placing in the scheme of things.

Irrespective of how long it is destined to endure, the earth is an old planet, and life has existed here in some shape throughout most of the past. During this time it has managed to reach everywhere that water and temperature permit, assuming such forms as may be necessary for long survival. Generally speaking, the more peculiar the conditions the more specialized the form of life, such as the flowers of fantasy in a tropical forest that depend on bats for pollination. Or the grotesque fish and other creatures of the ocean abyss where all but the living is darkness, where temperatures are forever close to freezing and pressures are tremendous, and the actual source of food is the dead and disintegrating organisms of the sunlit waters several miles overhead, falling like manna from heaven; it is a world of large eyes and no eyes, of living lights for those who can see, of gelatinous bodies, and of males who become actual parasites upon any female of the species that they encounter, lest they never meet one again in the all-pervading dark.

All such as these have a special fascination because they make an immediate visual impression. Other features of living things are more significant but have to be thought about rather than seen. One of them consists of the salts and water in your blood and tissues, for the past lives within us in a chemical as well as in a visible form.

In an uncannily complete way the sea persists in our blood and lymph and in that of most other creatures, although in a somewhat diluted state. Tears are salty and so is blood, and not just salty in a table salt way. If this was the only clue we might still suspect that at some time we had come out of the sea, although as a matter of fact all the fossils confirm it. The salty juices of animals are mainly solutions of common sodium salt, to be sure, but there are others as well, particularly those of potassium and calcium. Only when the calcium salts are in proper proportion to the rest can living protoplasm be its natural self: tip the balance in favor of calcium and the stuff gets stiff and lifeless; tip it the other way and cells become too sloppy to work; only when the ratio is rigidly kept can protoplasm maintain itself in its precarious position between two extremes. And the living ratio is the same as in the sea.

Whether the first primitive semblances to life began in the sea or not, there is little doubt that much of the earlier phases progressed there. In any case, our choice of sites is greatly restricted: freshwater, saltwater, land and air; and in view of the predominantly watery nature of the living, we are narrowed down to a choice of water that is either salt or fresh—with most of the evidence favoring the salt. All points to the sea as the cradle of life and perhaps the womb itself.

Without taking up the tale in detail, there is little or no doubt that the history of life throughout the ages has been a restless shifting from one region to another—from the salt seas to the realms of freshwater, and from there to the land; and in many instances all the way back again. Only in a few unimportant cases has the passage between sea and land or between land and sea been the direct one—the transition is too abrupt in almost every way. And while the various migrations and colonizations are each fascinating in themselves they are not our present concern, for in all these comings and goings there is a general trend which has little to do with specific geography. In a very real sense we see travel leading to independence, although you could say with equal truth that independence leads to travel, much as in the alternatives: do birds fly because they have wings or do they have wings in order to fly?

To a very great extent evolution has been a matter of discovering what lies over the hill, but not necessarily with any conscious or even unconscious desire to go anywhere in particular but more as sort of evolutionary restlessness that may be likened to a divine dissatisfaction with the *status quo*. Sea snails crawl over the sea floor, carrying their heavy protective burden of shell upon their backs, as successfully as they did in the Cambrian era of five hundred million years ago; but several of their kind have reduced the weight of the shell and have gloriously if somewhat awkwardly flapped their way to the ocean surface, to be labeled by human observers as the butterflies of the sea. The same reduction of a load of armor went hand in hand with the creation of living submarine rockets in the shape of squid, small or giant, whose ancestral forms were large-eyed mollusks browsing sluggishly in shallow seas with more burdensome shells to pull around than any other creature has ever possessed. Traveling fast means traveling light and this has been a rule from the very start, although neither one comes before the other. Only as the load is lightened does power produce the greater speed—as a gradual acceleration taking place throughout millions of years.

Backboned creatures have had a similar early history. The oldest forms of fish and prefish, judging from their fossils, were encased in heavy bony armor virtually from head to tail and spent their lives scurrying near the bottom of rivers and lakes. Only as they dissolved their restricting coat did they acquire the mobility associated with their name. The old-fashioned armored tanks died out and their several lines of descendants are all essentially powerful masses of streamlined muscle with as light an internal skeleton as possible and unencumbered by outer armor, so that salmon and sturgeon now drive a thousand miles and more from the sea to reach their river spawning beds, and slippery sinuous eels leave their ponds and streams on journeys that traverse much of the Atlantic Ocean.

Travel of this sort requires more than one kind of independence. Sea butterflies and squid have cast off the shackles of gravity, but the migrating fish have done more than that. Not only do they defy the pull of the earth and even make use of it for informational and directional purposes, but they move freely between salt and freshwater, in either direction. They have managed to form an effective barrier between their own inner environment—the body fluids which bathe their tissues —and the fresh or salt water of the outer world. No matter where they go, the chemical and physical environment within the body remains the same—they carry it with them—though the barrier itself may be little more than calcium-rich slime covering the naked surfaces, plus some tricky work done by the kidneys.

So freedom begins. Fish that first became fish in the freshwaters of the earth have several times, long ago, made the passage to the sea and extended their sway throughout the oceans. Others that never went to sea eventually managed to leave the water completely as the emergent four-footed creatures that have taken their turns to rule the land. In this case circumstances undoubtedly led them along the primrose path: as fish they evolved a pair of lungs in addition to their gills, as a general contribution to efficiency in waters that might all too often become too stagnant. Flimsy fins became fleshy and strong as an aid to getting from one area of water of sufficient depth to another in the prevailing swampy regions. Large yolky eggs in shells were formed and laid for safety above the water's edge. In a general way fish were forced into fitness for living out of water before either need or opportunity really arose.

The situation is somewhat peculiar. Each step, such as lungs or limbs, was virtually called forth at different times by special needs, yet in the end, when taken together, they all add up to the basic equipment necessary for the final abandonment of water as the physical support of life. With the means for moving on land and for breathing air, with eggs and young packed ready in a bag, so to speak, it is no wonder that such creatures as these were ready to travel, or that their descendants have been doing so ever since.

Leaving the water, however, demanded increasingly powerful limbs for both lifting and propelling the body over the ground and, as an initial condition or passport for entering the new paradise, body fluids had to be confined so that no seepage or leakage occurred except under the strictest control and to the most limited extent. An impervious skin of scales and horny material effectively wrapped up the new arrivals so that not only the salts of the sea but the water itself was henceforth carried along wherever the owner went, whether into the desert as a tortoise or in the future as men into space.

In their own way, though much less is known concerning the manner and time of emergence on to the land, the insects and their terrestrial relatives have succeeded as land-living creatures by virtue of similar devices: an outer, impervious, and hard skin that served to keep water and salts within and also as material for the construction of limbs and other useful appendages; and yolky well-encased eggs that could and would develop out of water. And so even with plants: water-supported kinds grew woodier and better able to hold their tops up beyond the level of water, and step by little step wind-borne seeds replaced aqueous methods of reproduction. Finally the land as a whole became covered, more or less, by vegetation and two dominant groups of animals, the insects and the vertebrates—all still in need of both water and salts but with their requirements cut down as much as possible, with a minimum of waste.

When you look at this widescale accomplishment with objective detachment it takes on a degree of magnitude comparable to the proposed exploration of space and colonization of the nearest planets. If landing and living on Mars appear to be a fantastic dream or a form of mental escape, so would romping about on dry land have appeared to primitive fish had they the wits to look ahead.

Freedom is essentially emancipation from outside controls. No matter how powerfully agile an animal may be in the tropics or how completely stable the complex mineral solution bathing its tissues may be, or how well its eggs develop buried in the warm dry earth, chilly nights or too cool a wind or too long an exposure to an overheating sun can be disastrous or at least a disadvantage.

Death waits in various forms for bodies that are too cold or too cooked to be active. Control of temperature is as desirable as control of water for it enables an animal to remain active independently of external heat or cold, so long as fuel in the form of food can be supplied to the metabolic furnace. Yet only two kinds have managed to acquire it—the birds and the mammals—and independently of one another. And once again the evidence, such as it is, suggests that the control of body heat was practically imposed by excessive climatic warmth; that it was a response to the evolutionary choice of keep cool or be cooked to death. The outcome, however, has been a general liberty with regard to the temperature zones of the planet, so that both men and penguins now wander about Antarctica.

The final freedom, although only the mammals and not the birds have gained it, is the retention of the developing egg within the maternal body until the offspring is well formed and able to suckle and in some manner travel along. Mammals in general and humans in particular are organisms that have gained about as great a degree of physical freedom on this earth as it is possible to get. Even the albatross that glides around the world over the southern oceans is anchored to a few small islands when the time arrives for breeding. And among the mammals only man can survive on the glacial caps of Greenland or reach the planetary poles and peaks. He can do so of course by virtue of the shelter and fuel and food that he carries with him, but this practice is itself a continuation of the whole preceding trend toward independence. So far as has been necessary, though almost inadvertantly, we have bottled up our original environment inside our skin and in such a manner that every outward change is compensated for within, so that chemical, physical and mental serenity are maintained.

During the past few thousand years we have enclosed capsules of the outer environment as well, called houses, which we maintain as constant in various ways as possible with heating units, air conditioners and so-called modern conveniences. It is just an extension of the age-old practice. And if our projected travel in space eventually comes about, we will merely have increased our independence of the force of gravity and in a more precise form than ever will be taking along a typical and controlled sample of the only climate and conditions we can live in. Our forthcoming trip to Venus or the moon is simply the next stage along the path of emancipation that we started on when you and I were fish nudging one another in an old Silurian stream.

WALT

"*It is no small matter, this round and delicious globe
moving so exactly in its orbit forever and ever,
without one jolt or the untruth of a single second.*"

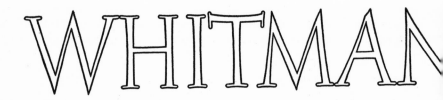

WHITMAN

14 : PLANETS AHEAD

Space travel is here, or so it seems, and the moon is naturally the first objective. We have come far since we worshiped her as Diana of the heavens and set up temples for lunatics in wooded glades, moonstruck and bewitched. Now the rockets are ready and mountaineers are waiting for a chance to climb the crater walls. The other planets beckon, too, especially Mars and Venus, our closest neighbors on either side, for just as moths fly to the nearest flame, we who can focus our eyes upon infinity are drawn toward the evening star. Granting the technical achievement, what are we going to find if we travel so far afield? Martian engineers, Venutians robed in white, curiously seductive lunar caterpillars, or nothing but dust and a clearer look at the universe? Or just a wonderful view of the earth before it fades from sight forever? The canals of Mars may of course exist in spite of no one having seen them for certain, and what lies beneath the cloudy mantle of Venus is anyone's guess. But the moon is naked as the day it was born.

135

The truth of the matter is that we are lonely. Having learned to talk and to communicate generally through a babel of language, we find that we are saying much the same things and thinking much the same thoughts, though making the most of our differences. The more we travel upon the earth the more we meet ourselves and the smaller the earth becomes. Fresh faces, even grotesque faces, so long as they are intelligent and, judging from science fiction, so long as they are aware of sex, would be more interesting than the white, yellow and brown shades of the single human pattern. Yet the real need is more basic than this, for we are deeply concerned with our human situation on this odd little planet drifting somewhere in space and time and we badly want to talk it over with someone. The solar system has become a neighborhood and space travel would have little meaning if we had no hope at all of finding some sort of life on other worlds. Making the trip to Mars and back merely for self-esteem and a little more scientific information would be hardly worth the candle, although since hope dies hard we will make it if we can.

Even without traveling, the answers are already coming in. No one now expects to find life on the moon for we can see enough from here to know what to expect. The image is all too clear—no fuzziness at the edge to indicate atmosphere, no softening of mountain ridges and crater rims to suggest erosion, no disturbance of the long straight streaks radiating from great meteoric impacts of long ago, no sign of air or water, not even a trace. We cannot see the back of the moon but the little planet does turn this way and that to some extent so that more than half of the whole is actually shown to us and there is little doubt the rest looks much the same. If, however, we do manage to set up an enclosure on the moon where men can live for a while, the lack of atmosphere will make the place ideal as an observatory for the universe at large and the earth in particular.

Yet in other ways the moon is an object lesson. It shows that just to be in the right place at the right time is not enough. So far as one can tell, the moon has been in existence for much the same period as the earth, and it is obviously as well placed with regard to the sun as we are, although as an abode for life, let alone for the creation of life, something is clearly wrong. To begin with, it does not spin fast enough, which may be the earth's fault rather than the moon's for mutual influence has been such that the moon produces tides in the earth and the earth causes the moon to keep one face always earth-centered—so that the sun's rays reach any particular place upon its surface only once a month. Days that are two weeks long alternate with nights of the same length, and at high noon the rocks of the sunny side are as hot as boiling water and at midnight have cooled to below that of liquid air. Life that is built out of water could not exist under such conditions and human settlers will have a little trouble maintaining their own temperature at the level compatible with survival. Even if the moon had a respectable atmosphere the overheating and overcooling would still occur and a much faster rate of spin would be necessary to even out the temperatures of day and night.

A more fundamental question is why has the moon no atmosphere? Without going to the heart of the matter the immediate answer is that if it had an atmosphere it couldn't keep it. The moon is too small and too light to hold on to either air or water at its surface for very long, and any gases or water vapor it might have had would have long ago drifted off into space, leaving the planetary crust exposed in all its crystalline purity to absorb the sun's heat by day and to lose it all by radiation at night.

As for the other planets as possible places where life might exist, all but two are readily disposed of. Mercury is not only small but is so near the sun it must be cooked directly through and through. On the other side, all those that lie beyond Mars, from Jupiter to Pluto, are from our point of view little more than frozen hells, though scientifically of very great interest in relation to the solar system as a whole. Mars and Venus, however, hold our attention most, partly because they are closest and therefore may be more easily reached than the others, and even more so because they alone lie within the possible water zone. Water could exist as such on Venus without necessarily turning into steam, even though the margin of safety is small; while on Mars there may be water as well as ice. Only the earth, with its abortive moon, moves in safety along the middle of the road. Yet what do we actually know of these traveling companions that lead and follow us around the sun?

Venus, that shines so brightly as the evening or the morning star, even to cast a shadow, and to be seen at times in full daylight, is often called the earth's twin sister. In size they are closely matched, Venus being just a little smaller, and we, if we were walking there, would feel our own weight just about the same as here. Venus also has an atmosphere so dense with clouds no view of its actual surface has yet been seen. Moreover, the planet receives twice the solar radiation as the earth and is consequently overheated. Put the two together, the clouds and the warmth, and one might expect that Venus would be a land of swampy, humid, fern forests like those of the earth in ages past. If such were the case and if the higher temperature induced a faster rate of evolution than here,

Venutians might very well have been coasting around our neighborhood in flying saucers for a good many million years and even have successfully colonized the earth, a possibility already made much of by writers of science fiction. Whether life has ever been possible on Venus depends, to a great extent, on how fast it spins. A couple of centuries ago astronomers saw rather vague or imagined markings which seemed to show that the period of rotation was roughly the same as the earth's, but later observations disproved this and suggested that, as the moon to the earth, Venus kept one face constantly toward the sun. If so, the sunlit side would be far too hot and the other too dark and probably too cold in spite of the heavy atmosphere. The dark side is now known to be too warm never to have seen the sun and the indication is that a complete turn is made between fifteen and twenty times in a Venerian year which is itself about two thirds as long as ours; in other words the day is roughly as long as a dozen earthly days, long enough to have a seasonal quality for any life that might be present. And in any case, the cloudy climate is in constant turmoil, with winds conducting heat from one part of its surface to another.

So far so good, but unfortunately some other facts of Venerian circumstances have come to light, or have failed to do so when they should, depending on your point of view. The trouble lies in what has been detected, and what so far has not been discerned in the atmosphere.

Whatever the kind of life that may be thought to exist beneath the veil of clouds, it must obey the laws of physics and have some means of producing energy, and the only sort of life we know here either splits up water to get at the energy of hydrogen, liberating oxygen as a by-product, as in plants, or uses oxygen for burning organic food as in the case of animals.

We cannot expect to find life of a kind that we would recognize as life except where there is some evidence of water and where oxygen can be found. The atmosphere of Venus shows not a trace of either. A real absence of water means that no life is present and a true absence of oxygen implies that there is no plant photosynthesis of the kind so successful on earth, for otherwise free oxygen would be produced in abundance. And if there is no oxygen, animal life as we understand it and experience it also cannot exist.

Yet none of this is conclusive. What is more discouraging is the discovery of large amounts of carbon dioxide in the atmosphere, indicating perhaps considerable volcanic activity but forcibly suggesting that living organisms are not around to convert it into living substance. Venus, then, remains a puzzle but certainly not an attractive prospect, for should the absence of water and oxygen and the presence of abundant carbon dioxide be typical of the outer layers as a whole, then we will have to look elsewhere for signs of life.

Mars is more hopeful in some ways, less appealing in others. Again recent history is a story of progressive disillusionment. A hundred or so years ago, Mars was seen to be a land of green seas and reddish continents, with polar caps of snow or ice, and an atmosphere with drifting clouds. Canal-like structures, which were seen later, passed across the green areas, so that the green seas had to change from water to something much more solid. Now the argument concerns the nature of the canals—are they canals of a constructed nature implying the existence, present or past, of intelligent animal-like beings, or are they natural markings relating to Martian geology? Photography so far has been unhelpful because of the fuzziness of our own atmosphere, and the human eye, aided by the telescope, may well have seen what the camera has not. At the same time, the human mind is wonderfully imaginative and inventive and much too readily sees what it would like to see.

However, what we know of Mars in other ways is not very promising. The planet is small, about half the diameter of the earth and has only a tenth of the mass of matter; the solar radiation it receives and the pull of gravity at its surface are each less than half of what is present here. It has an atmosphere, that is true, but it is far thinner than that at the top of Everest, much too thin for a man or any other earthly creature to endure. A generation ago observers studying the light reflected from Mars believed they detected at least traces of both water vapor and oxygen. Now even that bit of seeming evidence disappears when better instruments are used; and more carbon dioxide again is found than is desirable from our hopeful viewpoint.

The planet rotates almost exactly at the same rate as the earth so that the small amount of the sun's heat that reaches it is fairly well dissipated across its surface and the thin atmosphere is enough to serve as an insulating blanket to some extent, although without water vapor the effect is very small. At noon in the Martian tropics, which is a relative term, the temperature reaches about 40°F., dropping well below freezing at sunset. At night it continues to fall, probably to about twenty below zero. Clearly no lush vegetation can exist under conditions as dry and cold as these, and if we look around the earth for a comparable place we would find it in cold high-altitude deserts such as the plateau of Tibet. The white polar caps of Mars which wane and wax with the year were once thought to be frozen carbon dioxide, or dry ice, but the temperatures are too warm for this and the only alternative is snow or heavy frost, although the total quantity of water involved is not much more than would fill the basin of one of the Great Lakes.

The red color of Mars comes from the barren deserts of the northern hemisphere and the green areas originally considered to be seas are in the southern hemisphere extending up to a latitude of about forty degrees. These are the areas that show a seasonable change in color and encourage us to think that at least some form of vegetation lives there, even if our faith in canals and engineers weakens with each passing year. In winter the green areas become faint and either gray or brownish, but as spring returns and the southern polar cap begins to melt, a wave of quickening color spreads toward the equator, darkening and turning green as it goes. A regrowth of something must take place every year or else dust from the deserts would have obliterated it after millions of years, but what this something may be is hard to say. Plants comparable to the hardy encrusting lichens of our own planet might survive such circumstances, although the Martian types might not seem to us like plants of any kind. In the end this may be the reason we eventually make the trip through space, this and other information we would like to get, such as the chemical nature of the atmosphere and the electromagnetic fields of the planet, although excuse is a better word than reason. After all, no good reason existed for climbing Everest except that it stood so high and could not be ignored; as one mountaineer has said, Everest was climbed simply because it was there. And so with Mars and Venus, they are there and if we can reach them we will, which is itself a quality or quirk of human nature and therefore another fact of life of possible significance.

Taking the solar system as a whole, we may therefore look for life only within a certain orbital distance from the earth, roughly forty million miles closer to or farther from the sun.

Anywhere else is far too hot or far too cold, and only within the belt of possible water can life be expected to be, and only then if planetary mass and planetary spin make atmospheres and average temperatures compatible with the refinements of living things. And it follows that within such a belt an optimum location must exist. If that position is occupied by a particular planet, any other positions are likely to be less favorable if at any considerable distance in either direction. Two planets might find themselves well enough situated for creating life if they were located half way between the optimum orbit and the limit on either side, with only vacancy between them. In our own case it is quite clear that, spatially speaking, the earth is more or less ideally placed with regard to its distance from the sun and that the closest adjoining planets barely fall within the water zone. It is a question, however, whether a planet as small and light as Mars could have done much better, had it been where the earth is, in spite of a good spin, for its atmosphere and water supply would still be as small as they are. Whether Venus would be as the earth in the earth's position and vice versa are questions more difficult to decide. In any event life is here, abundant, rich in diversity and complexity, and exciting, tragic and joyful, because the earth as a planet is well made and apparently perfectly placed. For better or worse, we should thank the powers that be, whether they are conscious or not of their beneficence.

WALT

"I believe a leaf of grass is no less than the journey work of the stars."

WHITMAN

15 : THE ORIGIN OF LIFE

Life can be thought of as water kept at the right temperature in the right atmosphere in the right light for a long enough period of time. That, at least, is one way of looking at it. Another is that these are merely the right conditions for its expression and that the actual seeds, so to speak, come from somewhere remote in space—that life has evolved here but had its creation elsewhere.

The origin of life has been regarded as a mystery by human races throughout history, and most attempts to account for its presence have contained the germ of evolution or transformation of living forms in either symbolic or literal guise. The difficulty comes in conceiving a true beginning rather than some simple form of life, such as worms, as a place to start. Now that we have in a sense run life backward to a microscopic world, modern efforts become more and more concerned with the origin of single-celled organisms of minute dimensions. One theory, which was popular until a few

145

years ago, pushed the problem far away in space and time and effectively shelved it. Cells can be fast-frozen, for instance, to the temperature of liquid air and brought back to life again. The dried-out spores of microscopic organisms can stand extreme cold and absence of water for decades and still come alive if they fall into water. Spores of this sort are so small that the pressure of sunlight in outer space would drive them through the universe, given time enough. And such spores are almost certainly escaping from the outer layers of the atmosphere and drifting away as we take our spiral course around the Milky Way. If the earth can infect space in this way, so could any other planet where such life exists and a case can be made for an infective universe in which all planets pick up spores which then come to life and evolve wherever planetary conditions are suitable. As an answer to the primary problem it is no real answer at all, anymore than saying God created life in the long, long ago and started it on its course here and elsewhere. You may call this an answer but it is equivalent to saying that the question should not be asked since the answer is beyond our understanding. Yet the question has been asked and while we still see in the glass darkly, glimmerings of light are beginning to show some of the features.

In the first place, the cosmic spore suggestion fails to withstand the test. Spores of many kinds do drift about in the atmosphere and do become alive when they fall into water or moisture, but samples taken at various heights by air-borne investigators show that the higher the sample of air the greater the percentage of dead spores, and that above about ten thousand feet little potential life remains. Radiation, whether cosmic rays or ultraviolet light, becomes more intense the greater the altitude, and very few spores survive for long without protection. So we are forced back to the earth itself for any answer we can hope to find, although not necessarily to the earth as it now exists. Life of some sort has been here for a very long time and we are not only brought down to earth but are pushed back into the dim past to find the beginnings of what we now see around us, not only of life as such but of the world that gave it birth.

There are two approaches to the question, to work backward in time in an effort to uncover the past step by step, and to figure out if possible how this planet came into being and to see how conditions arose that could have favored the creation of life. And there is the matter of life itself which carries forever the imprint of its own birth. Whatever the course, our attention is drawn more and more to a consideration of planetary atmospheres, in particular to that of the earth at a time very remote from the present.

Setting the clock is the easiest part of the whole business. Radioactive substances have been widely employed or exploited in recent years to date the material in which they are found. From the very meaning of the term, any radioactive element, whether alone or in combination with other kinds, is unstable and in a continuous process of breaking down into more stable atoms, and in each case at a specific and constant rate. Radioactive strontium, for instance, which is the most feared of the fall-out substances from atom bomb explosions, converts to the safer kind at a certain pace, half of any given amount losing its radioactivity in about ninety years. Half of any initial quantity of the radioactive carbon produced in the atmosphere by the action of cosmic rays becomes inert in approximately five thousand years, and because of this it is possible to determine the age of carbon-containing materials if they are not older than about thirty thousand years. Farther back than that too little radioactive carbon survives for reasonably accurate estimation. Uranium, however, one of the two naturally occurring radioactive elements available for atomic fission and the production of atomic energy, has a half life of the order of a thousand million years—a built-in clock of no use at all for measuring events of the past few thousand or even the past few million years, but almost as it were designed to keep a record of the rocks. And, with an approximation to the truth, it tells us that certain microscopic plant-like fossils found in the oldest continental rocks in North America and in Africa are close to two thousand million years old and that the crust of the earth is at least a billion years older and probably considerably more. In other words, conditions suitable for some sort of life, so far as a substantial planetary surface and reasonable temperature are concerned, have existed for something like three billion years.

This is an enormous period of time and it can hardly be appraised except when placed against the main sequence of fossil-bearing rocks. The geological periods from the beginning of the Cambrian to the present, from the time of the first fossils of any size or abundance, and embracing the whole history of backboned animals from prefish to human beings, amount to almost five hundred million years, which is a very long time, especially when compared with the mere million years of purely human evolution, yet relatively short compared with the lapse of earthly time preceding it. Evolution on any sort of spectacular scale really entered its stride when four-fifths of the day had already passed, a fact of great significance, for it means that however slow were the early hesitant steps taken toward the creation and firm establishment of life, there was time and time and time enough for all manner of mistakes and recoveries and for new experiments. We cannot even think in terms of the time available and the time involved, except in an artificial and symbolic way.

So much for time. There are other matters. To start with, we can unravel the present atmosphere to some extent. When we go back to the beginnings that concern us, we are going back beyond the time when chlorophyll existed or in any case before it was employed on an effective scale. There was a time before chlorophyll because chlorophyll itself represents a tremendous evolutionary achievement and much must have gone on beforehand; studies of certain chemical isotopes of sulphur and oxygen in ancient rocks indicate when the green novelty first became important: well under one billion years ago. The importance lies in the relation of chlorophyll to the oxygen in the air. Eliminate chlorophyll and sooner or later the atmospheric oxygen will all have combined with the earth's rocky crust, and by the same token it follows that before the days of chlorophyll no free oxygen was present.

That is the first of the differences between now and then but a second follows immediately upon the first. Without a large amount of oxygen in the air no ozone can be present either, for ozone is simply ionized oxygen existing as a special band at an altitude of many thousand feet. We do not breathe it and it would be poisonous if we did, but we would find it difficult to survive here at the earth's surface if the ozone should disappear.

The ozone band shields us from the most dangerous part of the sun's radiation, which is the short-wave region of the ultraviolet. A little gets through, to be sure, but only the longer-wave-length ultraviolet light that joins on to the blue end of the visible spectrum. This is the light that gives us a tan and is active in producing vitamin D at the base of our skin and, given a long enough influence during a lifetime, often

turns skin cells into cancers. Weak as it is, it is both necessary
and dangerous to our health, while to creatures not usually
exposed to it and without any built-in protection, such as
earthworms and sea worms, even that which is reflected by a
blue northern sky has a deadly action within less than an
hour. The more intense ultraviolet light blocked in the ozone
belt would burn or blast most forms of life out of existence,
or at least all that lives upon the exposed land surfaces, just
as though you stood naked before a sun lamp all the time.

Before chlorophyll, then, there was no free oxygen and no
ozone where the ultraviolet stopped. The potent light reached
all the way down—into what? That is the question. Into shallow seas and warm springs and through an atmosphere undoubtedly different from what it is now, one that would probably choke us to death if we found ourselves attempting to
breathe it—a regular witches' brew exposed to sunlight as
vicious as lightning.

What sort of atmosphere and watery solutions enveloped
the solid earth during the time when life may have been in the
early phases of its making? By following the path backward,
all that we can reasonably be sure of is that there was no free
oxygen and that the most disturbing kind of light in the cosmos drove harshly through to the crust. The path was clear
for energy, and whatever stirred had no particular need for
oxygen. And we can surmise that insofar as the original atmosphere of the earth was very different from what it is now,
it was in all likelihood similar to that of the outer planets
where change has been kept at a minimum. In other words,
the earth also had a primitive atmosphere of ammonia, carbon
dioxide, perhaps methane and some water vapor. If so, such
an atmosphere is highly significant in a number of ways. In
the first place, the chemistry itself calls for attention. Water

is hydrogen combined with oxygen, ammonia is hydrogen combined with nitrogen, and methane is hydrogen combined with carbon; taken together they are the four fundamental elements that constitute the essential fabric of life—hydrogen, carbon, nitrogen and oxygen—all the raw material of the organic world present in abundant form.

How anything so complex as the simplest form of life, even a half-alive virus, could have arisen from such a gaseous mixture or even from some sort of watery solution of gases and minerals is a problem. Yet the problem is of the same kind, although of much greater difficulty, as that which faces the organic chemist in his laboratory every day as he attempts to synthetize complicated compounds from simple components. He may never succeed in reconstructing living protoplasm in its complete, dynamic and potent form, but he is already aiming at the virus and is in fair way of attaining it.

At the moment the debate runs strong. Several very different theories concerning the chemical origin or creation of life are being put forward and to some extent are being tested, and out of the interplay of minds and facts and probings the picture as a whole will slowly clarify. All agree, however, that the original circumstances were such that life grew out of them and the question is what the circumstances were and how did it happen.

One suggestion, which appears to be the hardest to swallow, is that living substance came into being as the result of chance combinations of the right ingredients. The ingredients were there, and certainly time was patient enough to wait for almost any event. The assumption in this theory is that the first living thing, however small and simple, was the result of a lucky shot in the dark, out of an almost infinite number of tries, and that all subsequent forms of life have stemmed from that primeval spark. It is conceivable, but the chances of such an event occurring are so unthinkably small that our credulity is stretched to the limit; even some biologists, who start with the thought that life did begin as a single microscopic occurrence at a particular place, feel constrained to bring in a supernatural intervention to get over the difficulty. And there is a further objection: if life as advanced and elaborate as a fully formed cell suddenly appeared as a single minute individual, whether as a result of an unbelievable chance or as an incomprehensible act by a watchful deity waiting to drop a little spice in the pot, the odds against such a cell surviving and multiplying over all the earth would also have been too great.

We are practically compelled to reject the lucky shot approach to life's origin, no matter how much of the right materials were lying around; nor can we throw up our hands and say it is an unsolvable mystery, a miracle, demanding divine intervention. Anything so ripe and ready as the earth must have been and so capable of carrying on from the beginnings of life to the present self-conscious, universe-scrutinizing age, could surely have taken that one particular, if critical, step with a masterful stride. Which leads to a very different approach.

Instead of looking for the origin of life down a microscope, so to speak, we might be better off using a telescope or whatever is necessary to take in the earth as a whole. Life can be looked upon as something which has happened to the world, not as a small local infection, but as a sort of envelopment of the entire surface—as a natural and inevitable stage in the evolution of the earth as a planet.

This is a matter of speculation, obviously, though not more so than trying to account for the shape of distant galaxies or the brightness of a star or even the nature of thought itself. The procedure is first to construct, either mathematically or tangibly or as mental imagery, models which might produce the results or effects you are concerned with. That does not mean you will thereby have stumbled upon the true explanation, only that you may have done so and that the more the model accounts for the better it is. If no model can be put to the test, the one that does the most to make sense out of chaos is the one generally adopted as the currently accepted theory. On the other hand, any model that can be tested is extremely valuable because you can then decide whether to accept it, discard it, or change it in some way. The in-coming atomic age of fissions and fusions, for example, is entirely the result of testing out various ideas and theories concerning how atoms of different kinds are put and held together. The successful results expressed by atom bombs and nuclear-powered submarines show that we have at least discovered something similar to the truth, although the little truth thus disclosed is clearly far from the whole truth, for the whole truth in any atom includes the mind of man as well as atomic energy.

So with the question of the origin of life. The first efforts at making models are already under way, although they have not as yet progressed very far. In all, however, the primary concern is the bridge or the step between the so-called inorganic and the organic world. For a long time this was considered the insuperable gap, the sharp line between a universal world that never had been alive and a world consisting of living organisms and their organic remains or their by-products. A bridge has now been constructed, whether or not it is similar to the original.

Theory came first, based up a number of observations, which was that intense ultraviolet light, in the absence of oxygen and ozone, reaching all the way through the atmosphere, introduced so much energy into the mixture of gases that chemical combinations took place which would not have occurred except under such duress. Put to the test, ammonia and carbon dioxide passing through a vacuum and exposed to the energy of an electric spark, and then bubbled through water, combine in such a way as to become several of the amino acids—the building blocks of the proteins which in turn are the structural fabric of all living matter. It makes little difference whether this model, so far as it goes, is exact or not. It establishes the general nature of the bridge and above all that some sort of effective bridge would have quickly come into existence under the prevailing circumstances.

A second line of attack is developing from the discovery that in certain hot springs, not far below the boiling point of water, certain bacteria and blue-green algae actually flourish; and also that at temperatures only twice as high some of the very simplest of carbon compounds unite together in stepwise fashion outside the body to form substances clearly related to the protoplasmic carriers of heredity. Neither chemical model may be better or more promising than the other, and in any case they are not the only two. Both are plausible, both lead to experimental testings and so to more discoveries, and both are compatible with the earthly conditions as we believe them to have been. In fact, they can be more or less put together to give us a picture of a primeval atmosphere exposed by day to light rays from the sun that would be lethal to us now, and so steamy hot that the light-compelled compounds went on uniting in ever-increasing complexities.

Everything seems to point in this direction, and it is awesome to contemplate, for if this was the general scheme of things, the image we get is that of the beginnings of life on a planetary scale—as a gassy envelope of hot steam, ammonia and carbon dioxide, exposed for hundreds of millions of years to light as savage as that of the mercury arc. There is no place or time where you can say life began, for it begins in a vague intangible way as a development or evolution of the atmosphere as a whole and this, if true, is really the most remarkable feature of it.

The next step follows naturally. As the earth's surface cools a little, from the temperature of hot steam to that of hot water —not much of a drop although a very significant one—what was more an aroma than a substantial reality now becomes a kind of hot soup with ammoniated vapors swirling above it and both white and black light still blazing away. And still there is no life in the sense of an organism, but the cooking proceeds at an increasing pace. You can put your finger in it if not yet upon it.

Such a soup, even if too thin to have much taste, may have been little more than a shallow and slightly salty lake covering much of the earth's crust, not necessarily more than would float a ship and not to be compared with the mass and depth of the oceans that have leaked out since those early days. Light could penetrate well and do its work, and convection currents would keep all in constant motion circulating to the surface. At the present a broth like this would have short shrift. Bacteria would embark on their biggest splurge of all time, multiply beyond measure and convert the organic richness into bacterial protoplasm and diverse smells, just as they would any defunct flesh or vegetation. Yet it did not happen then for the very simple reason that bacteria, like all other forms of individual life, were still a wave of the future. In the microbial sense the earth was sterile, but in every other sense it was potent with life.

This is where we have our roots, all of us, microbe, plant and animal: the primordial slime, although slime is not the word. From here on interactions proceed within the watery mixture and between it and the overlying atmosphere. Phosphates dissolved from the rocks and ammonia drawn from the atmosphere energize and reinforce the carbon combinations and gradually the fundamental chemistry of living matter comes into an established state of being. Life at this stage was the whole system of watery organic solution, atmosphere and light, all working together in unison, with no visible separation into individual organismal blobs and a seemingly distinct external environment. Even now the separation is really an illusion and the system is still a system working as a harmonious whole.

The road from soup to discrete protoplasmic particles and indiscrete flesh is a long one but it was taken. Of that there is little doubt, for we are here as proof, if that was the way it started. The journey was slow, in any event, and it may have taken as long to make cells out of soup as men out of cells, although which is the more remarkable is difficult to say.

This enormously long period of time between the first and second course of life is also the most important so far as the outcome is concerned, for what went into the cooking came out in the cake. The particular kind of cellular protoplasm that finally prevailed set the course for all that followed, but the long and involved process that led to its existence might well have been somewhat different, in which case so would everything that eventually grew out of it. The photosynthetic purple bacteria, for instance, might have taken the field instead of the green chlorophyll-laden algae, or any of a number of possible alternatives we know nothing about and probably never will. In any event a rich and diversified life would almost certainly have evolved, would have divided into some kind of vegetation dependent upon sunlight and salt solutions and so unable to move about too freely; and also into more animated forms, like animals, that fed upon the other and had to be more agile to do so, necessarily evolving means of locomotion, senses for orientation, and emergent minds in later evolutionary consequence. In every other way and in every detail, however, the course and shape of life would have been very different. Yet it all happened as we see it and experience it; and just as every choice you make is in some small way determined by this or that, so at every phase in the whole eternal process from planet to plankton and perambulator, the events of the moment set the stage for the next.

Accordingly, the right gases at the right temperature exposed long enough to the unfiltered light of a nearby star combine and transform into writhing, walking and eventually shouting forms of matter, which one of them calls life.

WALT

"*Out from the convolutions of this globe,*
This subtler astronomic orb than sun or moon, than Jupiter,
Venus, Mars,
This condensation of the universe."

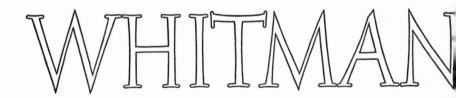
WHITMAN

16 : CRATERS AND COMETS

The moon is pocked-faced for all to see. The craters are there, to be accounted for and if possible conquered. Comets and shooting stars invade our spatial neighborhood and once in a while a meteorite lands on the earth with a crash. All belong to the solar system as surely as the sun itself and all have something to say. So do the planets, taken as a whole, the inner and outer and the major and minor, including all the bits and pieces known as the asteroids.

If you were some heat-resistant deity measuring off space outward from the sun and doubling the length of your pace with every step, you would come down on each of the planets in turn from Mercury to Pluto at the farthest edge if it were not for a gap between Mars and Jupiter. Almost as though creation caught its breath, a planet is missing where a planet should be. Yet not altogether, for that is where the asteroids are, most of them, in tens of thousands, ranging from the invisible to four that are more than one hundred miles across—

159

odd-shaped, for the most part, like Eros, which is fourteen miles long but only four wide.

What happened out there beyond Mars to account for the multitude of fragments that are flying about, making space travelers run the gantlet should they ever get that far from home? Either a planet-to-be failed to stick together or a well-finished product smashed up in some way. Could such a planet have supported living beings intelligent enough but dumb enough to have started an atomic chain reaction powerful enough to have blown it apart? Not likely, but considering our own recent and continuing state of jitters it is natural to ask the question. If the planet belonged where we think it did, roughly one hundred million miles farther from the sun than Mars, the reply is no. At that distance water would never be liquid and as we cannot imagine life in any other terms, such an explanation appears to be ruled out. What then? The answer, such as it is, lies at our feet, for the several kinds of meteorites scattered over the earth's surface have been carefully examined and analyzed, particularly during the past few years, and the facts seem to fit together in a remarkable way.

The heavy metallic meteorites have naturally received attention for the longest time, for their weight and circumstance make them rather obviously out of place. When they land, the general story is that of a fiery mass suddenly appearing in the sky and accompanied by sound like the thunder of guns. Throughout the ages the larger ones have usually been worshiped as having come from the gods, and even primitive man seems to have recognized their celestial origin. The "Black Stone" of the Kaaba, the holiest of holies of the Mohammedans, is undoubtedly a meteorite with its strange black crust.

In general, the metallic meteorites are composed of iron

and nickel, showing that matter from space is not different from matter on earth. When such a meteorite is cut and polished, however, and the cut surface etched, crystal structures appear of a size and pattern that could be produced only by a cooling process of a hot metal mixture, lasting over millions of years and under pressures of many thousand atmospheres. So what can we think except that the crystalline metallic meteorites were formed from the liquid metal deep in the interior of a fairly large planet? For only there would the pressures be great enough and the cooling slow enough to produce the structure observed. Microscopic examination even shows evidence of a sudden release of the tremendous pressure, as though by an explosive disruption.

Iron meteorites, however, also contain very small amounts of uranium, together with helium and lead produced by its decay. Estimates of the duration of uranium decay once again come out at about four and a half billion years. In other words, the meteoritic metal solidified from the liquid state as long ago as that, presumably during the early days of a planet of which it probably was a part. That was the beginning, but there was also an end, and here again the meteorites tell their own story. Not all the helium produced within the meteorites comes from the decay of uranium. Much of it comes, and in a distinguishable form, from the bombardment of the iron by cosmic rays. When the quantity of this sort of helium is known, the length of time the meteorites have been flying around as fragments incessantly subjected to the action of high-energy cosmic rays can be calculated. And for the four meteorites thus analyzed it turns out to be about three hundred million years—a long time, to be sure, but relatively recent compared with the age of the material itself. So it amounts to this: that a planet which first congealed four and a half billion years ago broke up with a bang a few hundred million years ago at the most, sometime during the great age of reptiles on the earth.

If this is what happened and the fragments still reaching us are some of its remains, we should be able to reconstruct the whole in much the same way that we reconstruct fossil skeletons out of a few bits and pieces. To begin with, the earth itself is believed to have a large metal core of nickel-iron, partly solid and partly liquid, surrounded by a mantle of very heavy stone nearly two thousand miles thick, and surmounted by a lighter crust of rock that is both thin and fragile. Mars and the moon, with diameters respectively half and a quarter that of the earth, having been astrophysically weighed and found wanting, appear to be much like the outer layers of the earth throughout. A planet, it seems, must be larger than Mars before the pull of gravity within itself is strong enough to have brought about a separation of its metal and stone, though it need not be as large as the earth. And the meteorites found lying about on the earth's surface, being of several kinds, show that just such a separation occurred. Some are nickel-iron similar to what the core of the earth is reckoned to be; some are mixtures of stone and iron; some are like our oldest rocks; and others, the lightest of all, are glass of a peculiar kind that is neither volcanic nor of human make. So the odds are in favor of a fairly large planet, although one alone is not enough if it was shattered by collision.

Supposing a pair of planets, one not unlike the earth in size and the other perhaps no larger than the moon had been born in the belt between Mars and Jupiter, why should they have had an accident? Planets are not likely to collide unless there is interference from a third party, and here may lie the answer, for the giant Jupiter circling nearby like a great magnet would have made its presence felt. Jupiter would have continually changed their individual orbits, and differently in the two cases. Sooner or later their paths would cross, and it was later rather than sooner when they did. They kept apart for more than four billion years, only to crash together in relatively recent solar system times. Perhaps the earth has been lucky in capturing and chaining its own moon without calamity.

Apart from size and swinging in dangerous company too close to Jupiter, what else can we say about the missing planet? In the first place, various minerals which are peculiar to the meteorites, particularly in the stony kinds, do not exist on earth for the reason that in the presence of water and oxygen they would soon be changed to other kinds. So water and oxygen were almost certainly absent from the crust and surface of the planet.

In addition to stone and iron meteorites, another kind lies widely scattered and shattered on the face of the earth. They are the small and glassy tektites which are found strewn across the Australian desert, over an area of more than two million square miles, far from any volcanoes that might possibly have produced them. Only their descent from space seems to fit all the facts, and it seems reasonable to suppose they have come from the same general region as the rest of the meteorites. If so, they represent the glassy surface of the broken planet. For just as metal sinks toward the center of a large planet in the making, and stony materials are left as the mantle and crust, so the lightest, which is glass, spills on to the surface to form a brittle skin. There is little doubt that the earth itself possessed such a glistening surface at the beginning of its career but water erosion has long since destroyed it. But without water as such, the lost planet retained its original coat until the time of its destruction. How such showers of meteoritic glass reached the earth is another question, though one that carries us one step further in reconstructing this or any other planet.

The tiny meteors that burn out as shooting stars as they enter our atmosphere and the larger meteorites that land with much of their substance intact are not the only wanderers in nearby space. There are also the comets, more than one hundred thousand of them, each showing its tail as it nears the sun on its wild flight from outer space. They are considered to have had their origin within the solar system, no matter how far into the void they travel before they return again. Yet their orbits are so fantastic it seems impossible the comets were born at the same time as the planets that swing in their orderly way around the sun. More likely they are pieces of the outer frozen envelope of our lost planet, like the icy crusts of Jupiter, sent careening out of course by the violent collision.

The spectrum of comets seems to confirm this view, for it shows them to consist largely of frozen gases such as ammonia, carbon dioxide, carbon monoxide and nitrogen. Each time a comet approaches the sun, much of this material is heated up and swept away by the pressure of light to form the comet's tail. With every visit the comet grows less and comets as such cannot have lived very long. So in every passing comet we actually see what might have been a planet's atmosphere, had the planet survived and had it spun its course a little nearer the sun. It would not have been an atmosphere that could have supported life as we know life to be now, but it would have been an atmosphere similar to what the earth most likely started with. Given a somewhat different place in the solar system and no companion to get in its way, the lost planet might well have flowered in its time and produced a living world to match the earth. As it was, it was born in sterility and died in catastrophe.

If the production of life is a cosmic intent, placing a planet where it ought to be relative to its star is only a part of the project. There are limits to size, both up and down; it must spin on its axis or it will suffer extremes; and it must swing serenely in its orbit without let or hindrance. The setting is familiar—the result of haphazard chance, apparent waste, and a precision in construction and outcome that has the beauty of perfection. Yet one is born at the expense of the rest. How well do they belong together and how are they made?

To begin with, the solar system needs to be seen with its components in their relation to the whole. The sun, of course, dominates in every way and is a thousand times heavier than Jupiter, which itself outweighs the rest of the planets together. All the planets lie exactly in the same plane, as though carved out of a single disk like the rings of Saturn, and the spacing of the planets outward from the sun follows a mathematical law. The sun itself rotates, completing a turn in about twenty-six days. The planets all move around the sun in almost perfect circles, revolving in the same direction as the sun's rotation. If the planets themselves rotate, they also turn in the same direction, and if they have moons, these too move in the same direction and in much the same plane. The system is orderly, harmonious, and significant, and the single spinning motion must have come from a single spinning cause. In other words, we must go back in time to a period when all of the matter in the solar system was united as one.

The most widely accepted theory at present starts with a dust cloud such as the seemingly small, round dark patches of dust scattered through the Milky Way. At a certain stage in its accumulation a dust cloud starts to contract in response to the force of gravity building up within it. Interstellar dust clouds rotate, though at first very slowly, perhaps little faster than a fly can walk. The Milky Way itself rotates and one would expect its parts to pick up the motion and, in fact, rotation of clouds in the Belt of Orion has been detected. The rest follows, more or less.

As the slowly rotating dust cloud contracts, it spins faster and faster. You see the principle in action in any twirling dancer, whether on stage or ice. Turning slowly with arms at first outstretched, they are then brought down to the sides of the body and as they do, the slow turn becomes a rapid spin. The physical law behind it does not have to be understood— you see it happening and that is enough. And the same thing holds for any revolving mass, whether of flesh or dust.

As the cloud contracts and the spin increases, the mass becomes first of all spherical and then begins to flatten out along its spinning axis, just as the earth has slightly flattened at the poles and bulges a little toward the equator because of its spin. When the original dust cloud has contracted to less than one thousandth of its original size and its rotation is rapid, a disk grows out of the equatorial material, in our own case when the mass had a diameter roughly that of the orbit of Mercury, the innermost planet. Then as the sun settled down to its present rate of spin, the disk was pushed farther and farther away, with the lighter materials extending the furthest.

This model of the way the solar system formed is but one of several and may be true in only a general way. It is, however, what is now widely accepted and is in sharp contrast to the older view which saw the planets as a broken-up streamer of matter drawn out of the sun by a near-collision with another star. In the new concept only one star or dust cloud is involved, and we are no longer faced by such remotely improbable chances as the close-collision theory implied.

How such a disk retains its revolving motion, or angular momentum, after it has separated from its parent body is another question, but more and more it appears that magnetic forces in some way are responsible and that the earth at least, together with the inner planets, is still connected with the sun by more force and matter than was realized. In significant ways the whole solar system is still all of one body.

The making of individual planets from the revolving disk of condensed dust is another matter that presents questions of its own. Yet here again the several theories are not too far apart and tend to reinforce one another. It is assumed to start with that the disk material was essentially the same as that which contracted to form the sun. The sun, however, contains a very small percentage of iron, magnesium and silicon compared with the four so-called inner terrestrial planets— Mercury, Venus, the earth and Mars. On the other hand, the outer giants—Jupiter, Saturn, Uranus and Neptune—are essentially light stuff. Saturn, for instance, would float in fresh water, while in water as salt as the Great Salt Lake even the others might do the same; they are for the most part enormous spheres of frozen gases, largely methane and ammonia. Differences such as these make the picture more complex, although at the same time it becomes easier to understand.

The contracting, revolving mass of dust was, until close to the end, dark and cold; and the evidence of the earth's crustal chemistry indicates that the planet grew together out of cold particles and lumps of matter and was never really molten hot except perhaps very briefly right at the finish. The arguments for this are intricate and convincing but need not be brought in here in detail. The important thing is to see the central sun, already hot and shining, and the warm material of the disk moving outward into the colder regions of space. Condensation proceeds as the temperature drops, the iron and silicates with their high boiling points liquefying or solidifying first; then farther out water, ammonia and other gases liquefy and freeze, while hydrogen as such, the predominant substance in the original cloud, never does condense and finally escapes from the system altogether, just as it escapes from the earth's atmosphere at the present time. Again, this is merely the sort of thing that went on and all we need to know is that it was an orderly process that could not readily have been very different. It leaves us with the question of planetary sizes and distances, and this is taken care of, more or less, by eddies or turbulence within the dusty disk. The size of the eddies increase from the inner to the outer margin of the disk, and this together with certain other matters accounts for the great differences in size of the planets and their mathematical spacing from the sun.

In the final phase each planet has grown out of local concentrations somewhat in miniature imitation of the condensing sun itself, and the satellites of the planets as small editions in turn. And in each case the finale has been a crescendo of bodies of stony iron, or of stone alone, or icy chunks, crashing inward with tremendous impact. The scars on the newly born earth have long since eroded away but on the moon you can see them still, where the last of the raining masses drove inward beneath the existing surface, throwing up crater walls to heights of more than twenty thousand feet, with centers one hundred and fifty miles wide, and sending radiating streaks of blasted rock as much as fifteen hundred miles across the planet. The moon is an unspoiled and still-born relic of the days of planetary birth, with all the scars of creation as clear as ever.

Such is the general picture of the origin of a solar system. The details are lacking and much of what we think is true may be off the mark, but in outline and in principle there is a fair degree of certainty about the method. We begin with a slowly rotating cloud of gas and dust and end with a sun surrounded by revolving, spinning planets at various distances from the center, a solar system consisting of a star and its satellites. And the evolution of such a system from blobs of gaseous matter may well be the rule rather than the exception. If so, our own system, with its sun, its one living planet and its several others, may be a typical sample of the galaxy as a whole—although in its own way unique down to the last little detail, including the face of each living thing.

WALT

"*O thou transcendent,*
Nameless, the fibre and the breath,
Light of the light, shedding forth universes, thou centre of them,
Thou mightier centre of the true, the good, the loving,
Thou moral, spiritual fountain—affection's source—thou
reservoir."

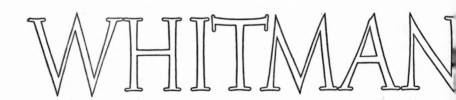

WHITMAN

17 : STARDUST

There is stardust in your eyes. What else could it be? Dust lies between the stars and out of it the stars, and their planets, are born and such life as they can bear. But what is the dust itself, and what is matter? Is it the same throughout what the astronomers, with a sense of oneness, call "the world," the entire universe?

We have arranged and numbered the elements from one to a hundred, from hydrogen, the first and lightest, to natural uranium, unstable at ninety-two, to the man-made trans-uranium elements that overstep the mark. The series is a beautiful sequence of central additions and rings about rings, with an eight-time rhythm running throughout. No more orderly and elegant a system exists in creation, and it is all a simple build-up from the simplest of all beginnings—in the minds of men, in the atom-smashing and atom-fusing machines of men, and in the stars.

Life, the earth, the planets at large, are forms of chemistry

171

—chemical compounds in wondrous combinations and accumulations, every chemical a constellation of atoms each consisting of a nucleus and its electron shells. Uranium fission bombs and hydrogen fusion bombs, the cobalt bombs for cancer, and that hope of humanity, the hydrogen-fusion process, have no real business here on earth and are nuclear matters alone. Whether they kill us, cure us, or lead to an abundant life, they belong properly in the stars, and possibly the most significant aspect of the coming atomic age is the testing out of stellar processes in the new atomic laboratories. To catch a star between your fingertips is a tricky and dangerous enterprise, but it is perhaps the one that leads most directly to the heart of things.

Atomic energy, so far as we have discovered it and hope to apply it, comes in two ways: the spontaneous splitting off of pieces of the nucleus of uranium and thorium atoms, which are atoms at the upper limits of size and complexity, like rocks that are piled too high—although a process that occurs at normal terrestrial temperatures; and the fusion of hydrogen nuclei to form helium, from number one to number two on the atomic scale, which takes place only at temperatures of several million degrees, temperatures that are stellar and unearthly to say the least. How firmly established the theory is behind it all is debatable, but the awesome applications to the weapons of war demonstrate its relation to reality, and we can extend it to the stars with considerable confidence.

To start with, the broad picture of the elements of the earth and stars and space itself is intriguing and significant. By spectroscopic means more than two thirds of the known elements have already been identified in the sun's outer layers, while meteorites contain the whole range of ninety-two from hydrogen to uranium except for the rare, inert gases which have mainly escaped from the earth as well. And although the list is far from complete, spectroscopic analysis indicates that the elements are represented more or less in their entirety throughout the universe, in stars and galaxies alike and in interstellar dust. We have no reason to suppose that in this truly elemental sense one region is fundamentally different from another, except in so far as stars and galaxies themselves may be in different phases of their individual processes of evolution. In this light our own star and galaxy are as typical as any other.

The striking feature of the elements throughout space is not so much their general distribution as their relative abundance, for it is the proportion of one to another that to a great extent tells the story of their creation. No matter where you look, hydrogen dominates the scene, with helium running a poor second. All the rest together amount to much less than one percent although, if we forget the hydrogen-helium foundation of the universe, the relative amounts of the ninety-odd trace elements are highly significant. Taking them in order, with hydrogen and helium as the overwhelming numbers one and two in the series, the next three, which are lithium, beryllium and boron, are virtually absent. Then in ascending quantities come carbon, nitrogen, oxygen, and neon which together comprise over ninety percent of everything that is not hydrogen and helium. Following these come a long series of somewhat heavier elements stretching from sodium to nickel with local peaks for magnesium, silicon, sulphur and iron. After that the quantities drop to minute fractions of even this last group, with the heaviest and highest elements, such as uranium, the rarest of all.

To one looking over this brief survey, several critical features are evident: the hydrogen foundation; the tremendous abundance of helium; carbon, following a peculiar absence of the preceding three elements; and the peaks at neon, silicon and last of all at iron. This is the pattern that concerns us most.

Hydrogen fuses to helium in the hydrogen bomb. Despite its threat to our existence this seemingly simple fact surely overshadows almost anything a bomb can do. It is the first step up the ladder of creation of matter, purposely and consciously designed by animated masses of matter that speak of themselves as human beings. Helium is not hydrogen nor in any way like it except as a gas that liquefies only at extremely low temperatures not far from the ultimate cold. The conversion of hydrogen to helium, a currency conversion of roughly one for four of the original, occurs only at temperatures so high that the chief problem in its control here on earth is to devise containers that do not themselves vaporize during the process. In the stars, however, no containers are needed and the very mass of a star effectively imprisons the matter within its depths. Stars, whatever else they may be in the universal scheme, appear to be the furnaces where matter is manufactured, a process technically but understandably called thermal cooking.

At temperatures between ten and fifty million degrees hydrogen is transformed to helium—a process called hydrogen burning because so much energy is given off, as the bomb itself testifies. If a star is all hydrogen to begin with, it soon accumulates a helium heart and the central temperatures rise, leading to the next step, which is helium burning. In stars known as red giants, where temperatures run between one and two hundred million degrees, helium transforms to carbon, oxygen and neon. The three rare elements in between are missing simply because they break up as fast as they are formed under these conditions, although they serve in the making of the others. Neon is the terminal of this phase, which is why it is so plentiful among the stars. Does it signify anything that we use it to put light and color in our streets at night?

Thus a star grows a deeper core consisting of oxygen and neon, surrounded by a mantle of burning helium and that in turn by one of hydrogen. The first and second transformations continue; but at the center it is the turn of neon to burn, at temperatures raised to a further order, at about one thousand million degrees. And in this new furnace magnesium, silicon, phosphorous, sulphur, chlorine, argon and calcium are created by the carbon, oxygen and neon. The star becomes more complex as layer upon layer of elements accumulate, until with a doubling or trebling of the central temperature, the group last formed changes to the so-called iron group consisting mainly of iron itself, together with nickel, chromium, manganese, cobalt and others, in the same relative amounts as are found in nature. This is at the center. At the surface of the star hydrogen still converts to helium, and all the successive processes continue depth by depth to the heart where iron and its compatriots are forming. Apart from the three missing light elements between helium and carbon, all the important ones are present with but a single great exception. This is the end of the first act, though what we see is as clearly a process of evolution as any that occurs in the realm of life—a progressive adding of one thing to another, with new qualities emerging at every step to form all the panoply of mineral matter.

From the point of view of life, our kind of life at least, whether animal or vegetal, such matter is incomplete. The notable absentee is nitrogen, for as the building chain of elements progressed, it passed through carbon to oxygen and neon without creating nitrogen on the way. Stars of the first generation, which are what we have been examining, do not lead to life directly, for carbon, oxygen and hydrogen alone, without nitrogen, cannot conceivably come alive, whatever the circumstances of a star and its surroundings. So a second act is necessary and it opens with a bang. (Whether you regard all this as fact or fancy depends upon your faith in nuclear physicists and astrochemists, for the evidence and the reasoning are their exclusive specialties. The threat of nuclear war and the promise of the atomic age, however, are realities already with us and they stem from the same understanding.)

Stars that have reached this last state are now in a precarious condition. The star begins to shrink and the internal temperatures rise sharply to somewhere around five thousand million degrees, when the heavy matter at the center changes suddenly back into helium—in other words a catastrophe occurs, and of this there seems to be no doubt, either on the basis of theoretical physics or from actual observation. The star blows up in the form of a supernova explosion. One of these is still in evidence as the so-called Crab nebula, which blew up in A.D. 1054 and was very carefully recorded at the time by Chinese astronomers. It is still expanding rapidly nine hundred years later, although in actuality the Crab nebula is so far away that its light takes almost three thousand years to reach us, so that we are that much behind the time and perhaps by now matters have somewhat settled down. In another three thousand years our descendants should know, if they haven't lost the records or the interest, and assuming of course that our race persists! As first seen in China the flare-up was described as visible, like Venus, by day, with pointed rays shooting out from it on all sides, reddish-white in color, and discernible for twenty-three days, presumably in daytime. Such explosions of giant stars at their peak are reckoned to occur about once in every four hundred years, which in the course of astronomical time adds up to a lot. When they do occur the explosion blasts the matter of the star to an immense distance, that of the Crab now being so widely extended that light takes about six years to pass through it.

So in the course of much time the original interstellar hydrogen, the gas predominating between the stars everywhere, becomes mixed with the elements created within the exploded stars. "Contaminated" is perhaps the better word since the stardust which has been added to the primeval gas amounts to such a minute fraction of the whole. Yet it makes all the difference.

Second-generation stars have come into being by essentially the same process as those of the first generation, only the process is no longer the cooking of an initially pure mass of hydrogen but the thermal cooking of a mass of adulterated hydrogen. The primordial hydrogen now contains some carbon, oxygen and neon right from the start, with even a small amount of iron. And once more the hydrogen of the core is processed to helium, but this time by a new mechanism involving carbon. A new path is taken toward the creation of the elements and naturally there are differences all along the line, the first and most important being the creation of nitrogen as the step immediately beyond carbon. Finally, when the second-generation stars in turn reach the red giant stage, element-making continues from where the first generation of red giants left off, building up from iron to lead and bismuth. And in due course, if the dust clouds and stars are large enough to start with, and have evolved into red giants, they in turn explode as supernovae and add their stuff to the space outside, so that stardust now consists of the whole range of the elements in roughly the proportions we are familiar with on earth, except for the great amounts of helium and neon and the overwhelming presence of hydrogen gas—gases which are in any case too light for the earth to retain. Wherever we look and however we look, the elemental picture is the same, whether in terrestrial and meteoritic matter; in light and radio waves from stars, nebulae and galaxies, and interstellar matter; in reflected light from the planets; and even in cosmic radiation. The universe is one and we are of it.

One radioactive element heavier even than uranium has recently been identified in the light emissions of certain kinds of giant stars: technetium—known on earth only in consequence of man's atomic monkeyshines—has such a short life it must be still in process of being manufactured or it would not be there to be seen; while another, californium, has been identified so far only in the hydrogen-bomb explosion at Bikini and, with reasonable certainty, in the spectrum of certain supernova explosions. Element-making goes on, heavier and heavier stuff is continually exploded into space, and stardust slowly but inevitably grows richer. And out of it stars continue to be made.

*   *   *

Looking back—as far as the mind can peer—we see a long period when the star furnaces created the elements in a protracted two-stage process of stellar thermal cooking, a process stupendous in scale and intensity and, from our standpoint, infinitely knowledgeable: an orderly evolution of elements of progressively emerging qualities and sudden novelty, with a second going-over to put in the oversights and extend the series. All as though an intelligent experimenter had the goal in mind but had to feel his way with the method. Yet the capacity to do all this is in some incomprehensible way a potentiality of hydrogen, the fundamental stuff of the universe as a whole. But order, certainty, chance and variety stand out as clearly as in the nature and history of life. There is as little fumbling in the making of matter as in the making of life. And in each case the question of time looms large, time that we can accept but cannot feel.

The trouble is that reason and mathematics lead to conclusions or statements which we cannot avoid accepting but cannot imagine because our personal experience and sensory equipment are simply unable to embrace the scope of things, particularly of time and space. Take time for a minute to look at time, in steps successively multiplied by ten; one year ago you can remember fairly sharply if you concentrate. Ten years ago you have difficulty in recalling at all precisely. One hundred years ago you were not here, though it may have been boyhood to your grandfather. One thousand years ago the Norman conquest of Britain had yet to take place, though many trees are alive that were high and mighty then. Ten thousand years ago there were no settled human communities anywhere, no villages, no crops, and all food was hunted or gathered where it was found. One million years ago mankind itself did not exist, only its prehuman forebears. Ten million years ago grass for the first time was spreading over much of the earth and animals were only more or less what they look like today. One hundred million years ago our ancestors and those of all other mammals were scared, nocturnal hide-and-seekers not much larger than a mouse. One thousand million years ago, all life was microscopic, and ten thousand million years ago there was neither earth nor sun nor yet a star. It is easy enough to put it this way, but your mind cannot really take in such tenfold jumps and in truth it is time out of mind. And still the time has meaning, for all things are relative.

First of all we can take the age of the earth and the meteorites as the age of the solar system as a whole. The material for analysis is abundant and close at hand, and the various long-term radioactive decay processes all give answers reasonably close together, indicating that the sun and the earth condensed to their present form and substance roughly about four and a half billion years ago. This is a figure of considerable certainty. And all the elements were already present at that time for otherwise they would not now be within the crust of the earth or in the material fragments that land upon it. Even though thermal cooking continues in the stars, the creation of the elements that make up our solar system and any other stars and planets of the same vintage must have taken place long before that. The question is, how long?

Elements that decay cannot live forever after they have once been formed, and when the rates of decay are known it is possible to calculate backward to the point in time where they were intact and no decay had started. Using uranium and its decay product, lead, the zero point appears to be about six billion years ago, or one and one half billion years before the solar system was born. Other methods yield a somewhat longer period, and even then we should remember that we are speaking of the stardust of second-generation stars.

Such is time and matter—time that is long but is far from eternal, and matter that consists of less than one hundred permanently built-up forms; a material evolution and as much time as is needed, culminating in stars and planetary systems, all based upon a single elemental gas. If you listen intently you can hear the universe singing its song of hydrogen, the first and the sustained note in the melody of creation.

WALT

"Thou pulse—thou motive of the stars, suns, systems,
That, circling, move in order, safe, harmonious,
Athwart the shapeless vastnesses of space,
How should I think, how breathe a single breath, how speak if
out of myself,
I could not launch to those superior universes?"

WHITMAN

18 : STARS AND GALAXIES

At last we come to face with space, not in the homey front-
yard sense of solar system space within possible rocket ship
range but the immensity that lies without, where even the
nearest stars are seen in the largest telescopes merely as points
of light. The night sky shines not only from the light of individual stars that make up the Milky Way galaxy but also from
the fainter light of far distant galaxies of similar kind. Con-
templating them, either the stars of the one we are part of,
or the galaxies of the universe, requires considerable courage
if we remain aware of ourselves and expect to keep our equa-
nimity. This may be the ultimate challenge, to stand foursquare
to the universal world and still know your worth.

Our own galaxy appears to be fairly typical, though it contains so much it might well be a universe in itself. Even its
space has to be described in terms of time rather than distance,
for light traveling at one hundred and eighty-six thousand miles
per second takes about one hundred thousand years to pass the

longest way through it. And its stars may be estimated but never counted. It is a planetary type of galaxy, meaning that it consists of a giant globe or sphere of stars fading outward into a globular haze, with a wide disk or girdle of spiraling stars and dust around it. The globe and its haze may constitute as much as ninety percent of the inhabitants, for the most part old stars of so-called Population II, perhaps one hundred thousand million of them. The spiral disk contains most of the stardust and most of the younger stars, those of Population I to which the sun belongs, but probably no more than a thousand million; new stars are forming here and many are relatively very young, some of them not only young but also of a short-lived kind with a life-expectancy as little as a million years. The sun thus becomes not only one among myriads but is lost in the crowd in one of the spiral arms, about twenty-four thousand light years from the center of the galaxy. And somewhat as the earth and its planetary companions circle round the sun, the sun itself, together with the spiral arms, moves slowly around the center of the galaxy, making the complete circle in about two hundred and twenty-five million years. Twenty rotations take us back to the time when the solar system came into being—a long time in years but not many times round the clock.

What is a galaxy, apart from shape and starry numbers? Clearly it is just as much a system as a solar system: it has form and motion and a definite constitution, and exists alone in space far isolated from others of its kind. And it has a history, as a whole and not just of its individual parts. Whatever its beginning may have been, stars and elements continue to be born within it, and all the stars within it with little doubt have been created there. Among themselves the stars vary greatly, tremendously in magnitude but not so much in mass, but all add up to the whole, contributing radiation at least, matter on occasion, and possibly planetary systems like our own. What we want to know is whether solar systems are likely to be rare or commonplace, or whether even a single other system such as ours exists at all.

When the nearest sun to our own is so far off that no telescope shows it as a disk, planets there or elsewhere are likely to remain forever invisible. Yet there is some positive indication of their existence, for certain minute disturbances in the motion of one or two nearby stars can be accounted for only if planets are circling around them. In a general way the prospect depends on how stars are made. Those that have formed from adulterated hydrogen in the manner of the sun are just as likely to possess their rings of satellites, and on this basis we can expect perhaps the majority of the Population I stars of the dusty spiral arms of the galaxy to be of this kind. Many will be too large or too small but possibly the majority fall in line with the sun and send life-giving light and warmth to one or more well-located planets. Such is our hope and it may well be true. But the old stars of the great central globe are in a different category. The chances are probably less, though no one knows; yet these older stars have preceded and apparently have laid the ground and supplied the nourishment for the richly laden spirals. At the least, they prepare the way for those that may bear living planets and at the best they may bring forth life on satellites of their own. Either alternative is in keeping with the profligacy and proficiency of nature as we know her here.

Not all galaxies are like the Milky Way or its larger sister, the Andromeda galaxy, close at hand in terms of intergalactic space, although more than two million light years away. Perhaps one half or more are spiral types like our own, while the rest are more or less globular and lack the spiral arms. Information concerning them is coming in fast, particularly through the use of the new radio telescopes, and many murky questions now troubling us may soon be answered, at least in part. For the present, certain significant features are already emerging. In the first place, the galaxies are not just scattered haphazardly through space. The Milky Way, for instance, is one of a group of about twenty located relatively close together. And so with the others—galactic clusters are the rule, many with more than one thousand members, suggesting that just as the stars within a galaxy have almost certainly been born within the galactic mass, so the galaxies of a cluster have at one time been united in a common source. Matter of some very tenuous sort in any case lies between the members. The process of formation is seen as a condensation of a supragalactic cloud of gas which separated into a number of distinct masses as time went on, each mass containing enough material to produce about ten thousand million suns of average size, enough for a single individual galaxy.

The overwhelming aspect of galaxies lies more in their numbers and distances. The other galaxies of our own cluster or family are mostly from one to two million light years away, far enough, to be sure, but actually separated from one another and us by about only ten times their own individual extent. Much greater distances separate one cluster from another, but the surveys show that the population is enormous, and that in the half of the sky that is dust free, that is, looking out into space from our somewhat unsatisfactory position in the edge of a dusty galaxy, a million average galaxies can be seen within a distance of one hundred million light years. A billion light years out, a billion galaxies may be seen, and this is but a minute part of the galaxy-populated space already within probing reach of our instruments, for the largest telescope now penetrates twice as far, while radio telescopes are receiving signals from even greater distances. We can no more make an actual count of the galaxies themselves than we can of the stars within our own galaxy, any more than we can count the blood cells in our body or the atoms in a cell. Estimates of reasonable accuracy can be made but not with any sense of actual number.

Nor can we appreciate the extent of known space, whether as distance or as the time it takes for light to travel. Light takes eight minutes to reach the earth from the sun, but light now reaches us from galaxies estimated at two billion light years away, meaning that the galaxies seen at the edge of the visible universe were there two billion years ago and the light they emitted then is only now reaching the earth. Meanwhile, of course, those galaxies have gone on their way and may be millions of light years farther off.

The situation is curious, to say the least. Here we are peering through telescopes from the surface of a little spinning planet and penetrate not merely space but time. You cannot, in fact, separate one from the other. We see the farthest galaxies as they were when life on earth was just getting under way in the form of microscopic cells but nothing larger; and during the time that the light has been speeding toward us at nearly two hundred thousand miles a second those single-cell organisms have evolved into creatures with large brains who are now analyzing and interpreting the ancient rays with sensory instruments they themselves have made.

What sort of light is it that reaches us from so far in the past and across so vast a space? The information it brings is both startling and significant. The light is redder than it should be, in comparison with nearer sources, suggesting that stars of the red giant type—the element builders—are far more common there than here, or were when that particular light started on its journey toward us so long ago. Two billion years ago galaxies were not only younger in time but younger in kind, evidence that the galaxies evolve like everything else that we have examined.

The other feature of the light from distant galaxies is a displacement of lines in the spectrum, known as the red shift, which does not mean that light is redder but that all the absorption bands of the elements seen in the visible spectrum are shifted toward the right, toward the red end. And it is known with certainty that light received from a star that is moving away from us shows a red shift while light from a star moving toward us shows a shift the other way.

The question is whether we can believe the evidence before our eyes, and the debate during recent years has been vigorous. More and more the answer appears to be that we can. In which case we are told by the light of the galaxies that those that are farthest away are traveling the fastest, and that the more distant ones are apparently moving away from us at a speed beginning to approach that of light itself. Equally, of course, we could say that our own galaxy is traveling away from the most distant ones at that speed, whatever it may be, for the movement is strictly relative. It amounts to this, taking the red shift at its face value, that the galaxies are moving away from one another at speeds more or less proportional to their distance apart, and that the universe as a whole is steadily expanding. The galaxies within a cluster appear to stay together and the expansion of space, if that is what it is, is primarily the space between the clusters. Galaxies moving apart at such a rate may seem at first thought to be dashing madly away from one another, but that is not so. Speed, like everything else, is relative, in this case to distance; and a system the size of the Milky Way moving at a speed of one fifth that of light would require half a million years to travel a distance equal to its own diameter, which is even slow when seen in that perspective.

There is one further point. The extent of the red shift of the most distant galaxies indicates a speed of recession faster than is directly proportional to their distance, which means, since we are receiving information that was sent on its way to us two billion years ago, that the rate of expansion was greater then than now. In other words the expansion process is slowing down.

Altogether we get a picture of a universe evolving as a whole, undergoing an expansion from an originally more compact state, but expanding at a slowing pace as time goes on. The description could equally be given for the development of an egg or the blossoming of a bud. It has all the marks of a true development, of an emergent evolution, during which each discrete part undergoes its own creative differentiation— from the whole to the clouds that have become the galactic clusters, from the galaxies to the stars and to the planets, and from the planets to life. System forms within systems and none can be truly taken alone, which, after some disposal of space and time, brings us back to earth and ourselves.

WALT

"*You unseen force, centripetal, centrifugal, through space's spread,*
Rapport of sun, moon, earth, and all the constellations,
What are the messages by you from distant stars to us? What
Sirius? What Capella?
What central heart—and you the pulse—vivifies all? What
boundless aggregate of all?
What subtle indirect and significance in you? What clue in you?
What fluid, vast identity?
Holding the universe with all its parts as one—as sailing in a
ship."

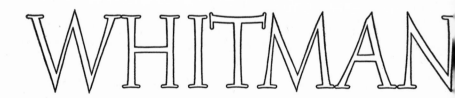
WHITMAN

19 : SPACE AND TIME

The universe lies around us immense in space and time, with or without end, and surging with force. What does it mean to us and what do we signify in the scheme of things, not only the human but all the fragile loveliness of earthly life? What is matter without a man, or starlight without a flower? Can we apply our own values to the cosmos as a whole and uphold the poet's insight that one crowded hour of glorious life is worth an age without a name? Can we challenge the infinite with the intimate and emerge victorious? It is worth the try.

Time is troublesome—for we have so little and there has been so much. Yet who knows what time is, if not ourselves; on this earth, who senses time except those with senses and a record of the past? Birds and mammals to some degree, not to mention bees, but human beings primarily. The others are unaware and only the present persists. We alone pretend to measure time, marking off seconds and minutes with a ticking clock, although even the clock would run fast or slow on another planet that was smaller or larger than the earth. Months are assigned to the moon and a year is a circle around the sun, though a man on Venus could count one hundred and twenty years before he died and still live no longer than his earthly three score and ten, while a month on Jupiter depends upon the moon you choose.

Planets and satellites and the sun itself have motion, but that is not time if that is all. An eternal waiting where nothing happens is not even waiting unless someone waits. Time, to be measured, demands awareness, and what is measured is change. It may be a rhythm or it may be progressive; it may lie within or without the being that senses it—the beating of a heart, the aging of the body, successive dawns, or the passing scene. Without memory there is no consciousness of time and without change there is nothing to remember.

Time can be projected or imagined as well as felt and stored away. We speak of mouse time as well as man time, though that has meaning to us and not to a mouse. A mouse, with luck, lives for two years and then dies of old age, living at a somewhat higher temperature and with a heart beating several times as fast. Its life burns furiously compared with a man's and its sense of a second is by no means the same. Nor is yours what it used to be or will one day become. Living time varies according to the species and weakens with age. So time out of mind takes on a new meaning.

So what is implied when we say that the solar system condensed to its present form about four and one half billion years ago? First of all, just that the earth has gone round the sun something like that number of times, although the sun itself has turned on its axis fourteen times as often, while Neptune at the outer edge of the system has managed to do the circle only once for every one hundred and sixty-five rounds made by the earth. It is relative in any case and it signifies very little how often unconscious matter has completed an imagined geometric circle—it could have been much more or less and made no difference. The importance lies in how much has happened while the circling motion has been going on.

We can for convenience cut the period into sections of a billion years apiece and those again into shorter segments, but we have no right to assume they have all the same value any more than we can truly say the sixth and sixtieth year in the life of a man contain the same amount of living time; for in the long days of childhood blood flows and wounds heal several times as fast as later on. Calendar time is but a rough and ready measure that serves mainly to show up reality, apart from its day to day utility in human affairs.

The true measure is one of content, even of quality, which is difficult to estimate. How much can be crowded into a minute and how little can a million years contain? More happened in a novel way during the second week following the onset of your own development than has happened to you since. How do you appraise it? A hummingbird beats its wings a hundred times while a tortoise raises an eyelid. A galaxy rotates about its center four or five times in a billion years. If it consisted of no more than a cloud of gas and dust, all you can say is that it has made the turns and the billion years has no meaning except to lives now living that have a significance of their own. In other words, we have no reason to be awed or overwhelmed by the apparent magnitude of time so-called that has preceded our own existence.

If first and second generation stars evolved from galactic clouds of cosmic gas and in so doing manufactured the few score elements of which the universe now consists, but nothing else, that is what matters and it signifies little to say that the process required one or more billion years before the sun and the rest of the solar system could have been formed. There is more to be said, perhaps, for the two billion years that followed, since this is the period extending from the consolidation of the earth to a stage when single-celled plant-like organisms were in existence, according to radioactive uranium dating methods. The events that carry the lighter elements through their successive molecular combinations to the staggering complexity, responsiveness and capacities of the living cell are truly of a new order compared with the nuclear chemistry of a star. More events occurred in this second compartment of time than in the first, even though the new events are restricted to the surface of small planets. Either time has grown richer or time has accelerated, from our point of view.

The next two billion years reach up to the present and cannot be taken all in one piece. How the first of these compares with the preceding billion years is not known. Life was still at the diffused microscopic level and has left too little trace. The pace of events may have increased but is still unimaginably slow for the human mind to contemplate. Yet that is the catch, for the events count and not how often equinox and solstice follow one another. Seasons matter only to bodies and minds that age with the succession and come quickly to their end.

Again, the past billion years must be subdivided. All we know of the whole is that during the first part the so-called Laurentian revolution took place that established chlorophyll vegetation as the major basis of planetary life; and that when the first half was over and the Cambrian period opened, the animal kingdom had come into manifold existence in all its basic diversity. A quickening is evident and although we do not know any of the details for lack of fossil record we can appraise the process by its outcome. And from here on time in a sense becomes tangible.

Calendar time has not changed but it becomes even less meaningful unless we project it simply as a series of markers like milestones along a road against which to measure acceleration of progress. In this way at least the acceleration becomes increasingly evident, as measured by the rate of revolutionary change accomplished during each successive hundred million years. In order to see it at all, however, it must be perceived as continuous change in the form and nature of living organisms, either in their totality or in terms of a particular kind such as the animals with backbones.

Primitive, finless, fish-like creatures changed to bigger and better fish with lungs and a tendency to crawl from swampy waters onto muddy land, with many sideline sorties to the sea. An evolutionary momentum is clearly present and impressive, but the transformation occupies more than two hundred million years, roughly half of remaining time. Another hundred and fifty million years see the emergence, rise and spectacular climax of the age of reptiles—giants on land, masters of the sea, and great flying creatures of the air—a period packed with drama. The shorter period is far more crowded with evolutionary events than the longer one preceding it. And less than a hundred million years later, the world has transformed and mammals and birds in tremendous variety inhabit a scene filled with deciduous trees, flowering plants and brightly colored insects, and again the shorter interval is much more compressed with a surging and diversifying life than the one before. Ten million years later the grasslands have spread far across the earth, creatures are fleeter, and apes are everywhere finding their feet—until, with less than one million years to go, subhuman forms appear and the final race is on. Such is the course of evolution, insofar as it leads in our direction, and in much the same way the past ten thousand years of human history show a comparable acceleration—in exploitation, transportation, communication and, far from least, in population. We all feel it, as though we are now traveling recklessly into the future, far out of control of where we are going. The sensation is like that of Alice with the Red Queen: "The most curious part of the thing was, that the trees and the other things round them never changed their places at all: however fast they went, they never seemed to pass anything. 'I wonder if all the things move along with us?' thought poor puzzled Alice. And the Queen seemed to guess her thoughts, for she cried 'Faster! Don't try to talk!' " Which is very much how we are.

Time, then, has its mysteries, to be sure, but the time that has passed is meaningful only in terms of what has happened, and we torture ourselves by projecting our own consciousness into the comparatively uneventful ages. If consciousness had been there, time would have been interminable. But such awareness has come late and the wonder is that it tries to embrace so much. The future is something else. It stretches before us in a calendar sense as far as the past extends the other way, if astrophysicists are right about the birth and destiny of the earth and sun, perhaps for another several thousand million years. This is time of another kind, the time that is felt and stored by mind, and is comparatively new in the world. What it may mean is not possible to say, for foresight and hindsight are very different, although if acceleration or increasing compression of events continues, the intensity of living becomes difficult to contemplate.

*   *   *

The immensity of space is like that of time and cannot properly be divorced from it, and also like time is never entirely empty, although relatively speaking most of it might well be so. The actual distances are just as far beyond our mental grasp. Even the distance between adjacent stars must needs be put in terms of light years, not in miles, although actual distances can be compared in a relative way: the nearest stars are about two hundred thousand times as far away as the distance from the earth to the sun; galaxies within a galactic cluster are several hundred thousand times as far apart as are the stars within a galaxy; and the clusters themselves are separated from one another by a further order of magnitude. Comparisons can be made but even at the speed of light no one actually thinks of space travel beyond the few closest stars. Talking about it is not the same.

Space is everywhere between the galaxies and between their individual stars, space mostly so transparent that the matter it may contain is recognized more from courtesy than conviction. The condensations of matter which constitute stars, planets and petunias take up so little space you could dash headlong through the universe without hitting a thing. One galaxy can sail right through another without causing any trouble apart from cleaning out some of the interstellar gas and thereby transmitting radio signals to be heard on earth. Even so-called solid matter is by no means what it seems. X rays slip through your softer tissues as though nothing was in the way, while heavy cosmic ray particles can drive at least ten thousand feet through the earth's crust without slowing down. Matter, whether liquid, crystal or individual atoms, in its most substantial form, contains far more space than anything else, in spite of impressions to the contrary. Space is just there to be accepted, for the internal patterns of events that we call atoms, solar systems, galaxies and whatever comes next all have much the same relationship to the space they occupy—all interesting, meaningful and difficult to grasp, but nothing to bother us unless we try to bring everything within our own personal dimensions. The vastness of space should not leave us cold and quaking but merely turn our thoughts more strongly to what lies within it, whether the planet that has produced us or the interrelationship of the universal world. Where space is empty there is little to think about and where space is occupied much may have happened, and whatever else it may be, space I am sure was never designed for any kind of human rapid-transit service—our mechanical age has gone to our heads.

If anything is fearful in the visible universe it is the uncountable number of stars. Our own galaxy alone is estimated to have about one hundred and twenty-five billion stars, which would require two thousand years to count at the rate of two per second. An enlarged photograph of the Milky Way taken through one of the larger telescopes is almost frightening in its presentation of the stellar community, the density of population is so overwhelming. And this particular galaxy to which the solar system belongs is itself but one of billions. We, as individual human beings, are simply not constructed to embrace such numerical magnitudes in other than symbolic mathematical form, but on the other hand neither should we feel lost and unimportant to be one among so many. As a solitary planetary system we may be inconspicuous, but so is the individual human. He does not thereby lose his dignity.

Time, space and matter must be taken together or not at all. We see the universal world with difficulty because of its stars, yet it exists nevertheless and space and time are but the warp and woof in which the starry patterns are woven. Order and unity emerge with ever-increasing clarity, with everything in its place in both time and space. We do not have to understand the whole to recognize its existence, and that we are part of it should give us faith in our significance.

WALT

"Ended our talk—The sum, concluding all we know of old or
modern learning, intuitions deep,
Of all Geologies—Histories—of all Astronomy—of Evolution,
Metaphysics, all,
Is, that we are all onward, onward, speeding slowly, surely
bettering,
Life, life in an endless march, an endless army, (no halt, but it is
duly over,)
The world, the race, the Soul—in space and time the universes,
All bound as is befitting each—all surely going somewhere."

WHITMAN

20 : YOU AND THE UNIVERSE

In the beginning there was light and in the end there was man. So the question remains—is life a by-product of but one odd little planet or is it widespread throughout the universe as the main event? The decision is primarily one of value, the relative importance of quantity and quality.

Space, time and stellar and galactic numbers hardly concern us here. They all lead to stars and in the last analysis the question is whether a star has meaning in its own right or only in relation to its living dependencies.

What is a star? A center of radiation and an element-building furnace, on a scale and of an intensity that would vaporize a planet that came too close, let alone the life it might possess. If this were all, if only stars existed and from their surface to their depth the various elements from helium to uranium were in process of creation, there would still be much to wonder at. The ascending sequence of the elements alone presents an exquisite pageant of increasing order, complexity and even beauty, with great novelty at every step. The emergent evolution of the material universe as exhibited in every star is a delight to contemplate. Yet what is it without a mind, and where is wonder? And if all stars are doing more or less the same thing, are all manufacturing, in one phase or another, a single series of elements and one continuous range of radiation, then a billion billion billion of them offer little more to marvel at than the solitary performer. Values lie in unique individuals whether of stars or men. If every human was the same as every other in shape and thought and action, if everyone you met was yourself once over, it would signify little how many you were.

Numbers and magnitudes overawe us or they do not. We are capable of judgment. It is as simple as that. We judge a star burning hydrogen to helium to mean more than a cloud of hydrogen however large, and a star that creates all the elements to mean more again. More happens and matter becomes far more complex and significant. We recognize this intuitively, by a form of comprehension that lies deeper than reason or logic. And if we accept our judgment as valid, the rest follows: a star with planetary satellites is more significant than one without, if only because its pattern and history are more complex; while a planet with but a single living cell, if that were possible, would be as worthy of attention as Friday's footstep in the sand.

On this ground we can more than match the heavenly powers, if such a contest makes sense. Even the crystals of the rocks possess an elaborate elegance unmatched by any star, while the simplest forms of life are complex beyond measure. It is here, on earth, that the greatest qualitative events have taken place. For organisms, large or small, are the counterparts to the sun, and all have a majesty of their own. They are the natural extensions of solar creation under conditions that are incompatible with either the surface or interior of a star. Just as the whole range of the elements are in some way implicit in the nature of hydrogen from which they evolve, so molecules, crystals and life itself are immanent in stellar matter but require conditions of temperature, pressure and gravity that are very different. The evolutionary process is continuous from hydrogen through the nuclear elements to molecules and living things and minds—there is no break in the material basis, only a wonderful and staggering progressive transformation. And only as a whole can we make sense of it. Life of every kind depends upon the sun for its hour to hour existence—our own dependence is far too clear. On the other hand, the sun alone is too much like a fire on a winter's night with nobody beside it. The radiation warms no one, reaches nowhere and lights up nothing. As a creative process it fails to fulfill its own promise.

If the sun, or any other star, is the power and glory, loveliness is linked to a planet. In our specifically human eyes other creatures may be handsome or horrible and plants may be beautiful or grotesque, or we may take them all for granted as either useful or a nuisance. Yet they all consist of elements produced within the stars, and each and everyone is an accumulation of organized matter that has much the same relationship to the stripped atoms within the sun as the greatest poem or prayer has to the letters of the alphabet. The analogy is not far-fetched, for both letters and elements contain the potentiality of greatness, and both can remain but a jumbled assembly of what might have been.

Universal evolution shows a definite trend from the large and diffuse to the small, concentrated and precious. More than nine-tenths of the atoms of the universe are hydrogen, of which more drifts about as gas than is contained within the stars. Nearly three-fourths of the remaining atoms are helium, and the two together constitute the bulk of the stars. The atoms of the lighter elements out of which planetary atmospheres and crusts and living organisms are made amount to about one-tenth of one percent of these, while the metals from iron to uranium add up to only one-tenth of that again. The higher the fewer is a cosmic rule, and so with life. Multitudinous microorganisms sustain and lead to larger but fewer organisms of a more complicated nature, and these in turn lead to bigger and better and fewer again. With each step up, the number drops to a minute fraction of those on the one below. And with each upward step a great increase occurs in the number of atoms adhering together as a living unit. This perhaps is the truly remarkable aspect of it all: the steady building of little units into bigger ones—hydrogen nuclei and electrons successively into the whole chain of elements; atoms and simple molecules into the giant proteins; proteins and other molecular complexities into free-living cells; cells into many-celled organisms and all the way to whales and redwoods and human brains. It is all of a piece and the only interruption is a planet. By the nature of things, how else could it be accomshift of scene from the interior of a star to the surface of a plished? If life is as much the purpose of universal development as a chick is ordained in the egg, it is no more surprising that a star requires a small satellite at a certain distance than that the formation of the elements results from cooking in two or three generations of exploding stars instead of all being produced neatly at one place and time. We should take the universe at its face value and accept it as we find it. And that includes the face of man looking outward at the rest, inward into himself, and to past and future time. If the system still seems a lot to make a little, that is the way it is, and the rule applies all along the line and neither a man nor a bee is dwarfed by the greatness of its sun.

There is an exquisite beauty of perfection in every sort of life, whatever its form and action may seem to us. A fitness and a fragility go hand in hand, ready to vanish at a cosmic breath or flourish if all goes well. All life is delicate to an extreme and if life gives meaning to the stars it is remarkable that so seemingly rough and ready methods should result in such precision—that life, once produced, should persist and continually transcend itself for two or three billion years. Yet this is the case and we ourselves embody it more than the rest of the living world, for we alone look beyond the earth in space and time.

What, then, is a man, apart from his troubles and joys and the havoc he creates around him? If you regard him as matter that has come out of a sun, you have your answer, at least in part: stardust on a planet's surface, concentrated into living form, of living substance with a past half as old as the stars themselves—sensitive to cosmic forces, part of a community and a stream of life, reconstructing the universe as a whole within his brain, recognizing perfection and loving it, and sorrowing over the brevity of his own consciousness. If we accept all this, the consciousness and self-consciousness included, as natural an emergence of evolving matter as water condensing from steam, our gain is immeasurable. That even one planet in the universe can produce the human organism, let alone the pageant of life around it, is as striking as if a solitary peacock were found upon the moon. It speaks for itself, whether or not its language is understood.

Much less than a man is needed to speak for the earth. Our mental feats and range of appreciation may set us aside and give us the greatest claim to be its spokesman, yet we are still but a part of earthly living nature and we should never lose sight of its diversity and wholeness throughout the present and the past. Taken altogether it is rich almost beyond belief. If such as this is a built-in potentiality or capacity of stellar matter, including our thoughts about it, one thing is certain: that we, speaking now for all terrestrial life, cannot be odd man out but must be as typical a symbol of the universe as any twinkling star, although it does not follow that even the majority of stars have planetary systems any more than all planets should bear life.

How commonplace solar systems may be depends on how they are produced. If current theories of star formation are more or less correct and stars form from great masses of slowly revolving gas and dust, progressively condensing and spinning evermore rapidly, until at last a planetary disk of matter extends from the rotating equator somewhat like the rings of Saturn, solar systems may well be the rule. The older theory that planetary matter was drawn out of the sun by a near-collision with another star is now discarded and the remote chance of such an event no longer needs to discourage us from thinking of the universe as essentially alive. Each of the several theories now in favor regard the planetary systems as a natural development or evolution of a single star, with no chancy assistance from any other source. The question therefore boils down to which of the various types of stars are likely to have become solar systems and which are not. There is no need here to make an extensive survey or to probe very far into star evolution, only to recognize that two large classes of stars are disqualified, although their contributions to the whole super-system may in other ways be indispensible. These are the stars that have been or are considerably larger than the sun, which burn up and blaze out in far too short a time for planets to have a chance; and the stars that are far older than the sun, those that comprise the great spherical central mass of a galaxy and its haze of globular clusters, usually spoken of as Population II.

The Population II stars are older by one or two billion years than those of the spiral mars of a galaxy such as our own, and appear to be almost exclusively formed of hydrogen and helium. If this is so, any planetary disk they may have possessed would have soon been driven away as gas and in any event could not have formed the stuff of which planets are made, in which case the majority of stars are without planetary satellites. The stars of the spiral arms and disk of the elliptical galaxies, the Population I stars, are not only younger but are more or less enveloped in the richer stardust of the kind that gave them birth. Our sun is one of them and of an average size—and all such are likely to have planets around them; and though a minority in the total picture, they constitute a large minority. That stars of this kind may be numerically outclassed, however, is merely in keeping with the pyramidal structure of evolution—the more differentiated stars require a broader base of primary stars as a prelude to their own existence. Even so, if all stars of about the same age, size, spin and general location as the sun have planetary systems, our own galaxy alone has roughly ten thousand million—enough to make sense of the rest—and so with the uncountable other galaxies of similar kind.

On this reckoning the star systems as a whole are means of producing and perpetuating stardust and solar systems, and in the same vein solar systems are devices for forcing matter to become alive and flow in time through transcendent forms. Once more the system must act as a system to carry meaning, for while a planet at best is dead and cold without a sun and a planetless sun can blaze away in sterile grandeur, together they sing the song of life in a harmony that is unmistakable.

In a series of planets only one, or possibly two, can be in the right relationship to its star, as the earth is to the sun, and it is this particular partnership that counts. The planet, if it is large enough, supplies the substrate or emulsion, so to speak, holding an atmosphere to its surface and squeezing out a salty ocean through its stony crust, while heat rays and light rays from the sun maintain the temperature and drive the chemistry from mineral to mind, developing the living pattern and building stronger and sharper images all the time. And once again the system works on a self-feeding, self-transforming principle—from first to last, life is not only part and parcel of its environment but transforms the very air and rocks as it progresses, and in turn reacts to the changes it brings about. Action and reaction is the rule and out of it grows the mounting pace and stature of the living earth. Microbes, plants, animals and mineral nature all combine as a single dynamic whole persisting in pulsing vibrant form throughout time and it is only within this mesh of existence that human beings have any context.

Where is man, specifically, in this web of evolution? Only relative answers are possible. We are now, at this time and place, six or seven billion years from the birth phase of the oldest stars and the probable origin of matter other than primeval gas; and we are between four and five billion years from the birth of the sun and the earth. More importantly, perhaps, we are about three billion years from the time of onset of terrestrial life. That we happen to be part of this particular solar system situated in one particular location in a spiral arm of this particular galaxy is a situation we have simply to accept, just as you accept the fact that you are you, and not some other individual—if a question lurks here, it is not one that can be properly asked. In any case we are the product of some three billion years of stellar evolution and of much the same duration of essentially living development. That has been our history and it is well to ponder it. And with this in mind it is startling to realize that as distinctively human beings with anything approaching our present mental capacity we have been here for less than one million years, which is but one fifth of one percent of the time backboned creatures have existed and a much smaller fraction of the living total. Against this time-scale of creation, whether of stars, planets or life itself, we have just happened—and only now, in the past second or two of our own human phase, do we look around to see where we are and to wonder what we are. It is not surprising that we are dewy-eyed and still more or less confused by what we see.

If this is an evolutionary universe, as the majority of astronomers and their kind believe it to be, and the galaxies as such are of about the same age, dust cloud stars are nowhere much older than the sun. It follows, therefore, that nowhere has there been more time for the creation of bodies and minds than there has been here. A slight shift of the earth's orbit toward the Sun might have resulted in a quickening of the evolutionary pace and possibly in other systems the favored planet is so placed and life may be ahead to some degree. But it is not certain that such would be the effect and, although solar systems may be continually coming into existence in the dusty arms of galaxies, our own system is likely to be as old as any and the earth is about as well placed as we can imagine; in which case our recent emergence as universe-conscious creatures takes on a new significance.

Looking at the human organism as objectively as possible and putting down the natural tendency to self-inflation, something happened in the transition from lower anthropoid to man that is essentially a break-through to a new level of mental capacity that is so different in degree, if not in kind, that it is virtually a new order of existence. Whether or not we succeed in holding the future in our hands and continue the trend of the immediate past toward bigger and better brains, and all that goes with them, we are a fact, we are here, we are new in time and it is difficult to see how we, in our particular form, could have been produced any sooner.

Every solar system that produces life at all makes it in its own image and not ours, and the chance that anything with human shape or even human chemistry exists anywhere except on this earth is remote indeed. At the same time the basic division of life into photosynthetic and more animated types is likely to occur and among the latter, senses and brains of some sort are probably as inevitable elsewhere as here—and insofar as mind of the quality we already possess appears to be an emergent from a lesser kind, mind must be regarded as a predictable though a late-flowering product of a well placed, adequately constructed planet in any solar system worthy of the name. If minds of a quality at least more or less equivalent to our own, whatever their embodiment may be, are to be expected on similarly situated planets throughout the universe, we can look upon our own as one blossom in a field of flowers, opening its petals toward the light, perhaps a little sooner or a little later than the others but generally in keeping with the time of day. If such is the nature of our flowering, our need is to comprehend the world of light above us and to realize that our roots go deep into the earth; and to appreciate fully the variety of other life that surrounds us, without wanting to crowd it all into the ditch.

This is the beginning, not the end. Stars add up to galactic systems in which new and richer stars are made, but what are men, as distinct from a man? Do we add up in any way or is the individual the unique creation in which all value lies? There is no clear answer, although a solitary person left alone in the world would know that he was lost and might as well cease to exist. I am aware also that I, like every other being, am wonderfully contrived, but I know that by myself I am not enough —the meaning goes, whatever it may be. The whole enterprise is too vast, too massively ruthless, to be making organisms even as self-conscious as you or I simply for fun. As individuals we do not stand alone and perhaps our most urgent problem is to understand our continuities.

Our own limitations stand in our way. The sense of the past is itself something new. Memory has never before extended beyond the life of an individual creature and usually for much less than that. Moreover, lives have been and for the most part are very short, and even human lives are remarkably long in comparison with the rest. And any probing of the past beyond the tribal tradition is a matter of the past few thousand years at the most. In any case the feeling of continuity with past life does not come easily, although it is one of the realities we have to grasp, for we, as the human race, let alone as individuals, are essentially as the buds on the ends of twigs of a tree, aware of the space between us but not the continuity of sap that has sustained us throughout time.

We suffer rather readily from the feeling that we are each of us something definite and stable like a chair or a spade, something you can rely on to be the same day in and day out apart from a little temperament. That is the illusion. The reality is that you and I, like all else that lives, are creatures of time. Not only do we change with time, obviously so in infancy, more subtly in middle age, but everything we are and do and think, is a process which is continuous with past events —in essence like a flowing stream or a burning flame. The continuity runs backward through time, from you as an organism to the germ you once were, to the maternal tissue of which that was a part, and so, generation by generation as a tenuous and rhythmically swelling line of action and substance, all the way to the beginnings of earthly life. By which time all other lives have run back to the same source, joining strand by strand and age by age, till all at last become one. That is the reality. We are continuous with our past selves and all our progenitors and sooner or later link up with those of all other living beings. There is no break, for these are life lines and any ruptures have been final, as many a frayed end shows us in the fossil record. This all-pervading oneness is vital in every sense of the word and our difficulty in appreciating it comes from our newly emergent evolutionary state and also most likely from the particular nature of our past, with its specifically anthropoid outlook and its resulting limitations as well as its potentialities.

Apart from intuition and apart from evolutionary reconstruction, altogether too much effort and ingenuity have gone into the making of any one of the more outstanding forms of life for the individual of whatever kind, or for that matter for any one race, to be the cherished darling of the gods. The living world is undoubtedly more than the sum of its parts—it would not be in keeping with its constituents were it not. But what the totality amounts to and where it is leading is a comprehension we are reaching for but have not yet attained—we have only the faith that it is real and a feeling that all we know about life and the universe confirms it. In fact, the fullness of reality may always elude us and what we sense now may be as much as the human organism is equipped to take.

To see it face to face could be overwhelming and may require an evolution far beyond our present somewhat half-baked stage.

What, then, is the human individual in a setting of uncountable galaxies, each with its myriads of stars? The same rule holds as here on earth. No two life-bearing planets will be alike, any more than are two human beings. Each in its own way will be unique, each will flower according to its own nature and sooner or later will inevitably create mind out of sensations, though never the same as another. As the earth has, or has had, its own lovely garment of diverse life, and as the individual and collective human minds have flourished in their own frequently breathtaking way, so throughout the universe comparable but unique creations are in process of fulfillment. Space may forever separate us as definitely as one man is from another, but not time and not the inborn adventurous spirit that seems to inhabit all that we call matter and particularly that which we call life. Nature, in the intimate and in the vast, is not designed. It is designing. Our own nature confirms it.

The nature of the universe is far more apparent in human qualities than in the atomic furnaces of the stars or the magnitudes of space. Insight into the nature of things is a recent emergent property of human matter. It appears to be reflecting the universe past and present. If all goes well the process will continue and evolve, and in the course of time, as we are and as we will become, we may understand the spiritual significance of the Milky Way—for as this earth has come alive and consciousness and sensitivity have come into being, so elsewhere throughout space wherever stars are seen. Separateness is the illusion and the signs of unity are those flashes of deeper insight that have transformed every man and woman who has experienced them. In the end, I am sure, we will sense the community of the cosmos as we are now painfully but certainly coming to know the brotherhood of man. Yet such an end will be but a new beginning, just as the creation of a united human community will in its own way be the true commencement of human life on earth, with all of its major problems and potentialities before it.

When we understand ourselves completely we will know the rest, for the universal meaning that we search for is imbedded here. Walt Whitman wrote that "the whole theory of the universe is directed unerringly at a single individual, namely, you," which is an overstatement, for in the literal sense of the peculiar human shape this is not so, except as one among many, yet in the deeper meaning it rings true. The emerging qualities of hope, courage, love, intellectual quest and the sense of beauty, as represented to some degree in every human being, are emergent qualities of all that the universe is made of, and here on earth they are beginning to shine with the light that never was on land or sea. This is your stature, as bearers of a flickering torch that has but recently been lighted. Whether you wish to call this the path to God or to use some other term is not important, for the meaning is far older than any language and is both supernal and transcendent. At this level the spiritual and scientific ventures become one, and any experience derived from either source must be scrutinized in the light of the other. Above all we need not be afraid, either of the universe at large in all its oneness and multiplicity, or of our own nature which has itself been created by a star.

If mind and spirit grow out of matter they are nonetheless what they have been thought to be. It is our conception of matter that needs revision. All that is included in thought, perception and spiritual harmony belong as naturally in the universe as visible energy and tangible matter, and it is our peculiarly human task at the moment to see them all as facets of a whole. If solar systems exist for the sake of life and mind, we who are now becoming conscious of the situation are under obligation to see it in its entirety. In religious language this means coming face to face with God, although the Godhead lies within rather than somewhere out in space or far back in time. The universe has had its history just as truly as mankind itself or as you as an individual person. It evolves as a whole and our own planet with its active and mental life has evolved with it in step with all the rest. What we now recognize as the divine may be the emergent future itself—spirit becoming manifest, not only here but throughout the universal world—struggling for expression with all the pangs of creative anguish, dependent upon life and long immanent in matter. The universe is as we find it and as we discover it within ourselves. You and I epitomize its nature and are the essence of its continuity. Individually we come and go but together we contain all of the past and carry the bright hope of a creative, adventurous universe—and not only here but wherever planets have been fully fertile, wherever a sun shines to bring forth glory.

CONTENTS

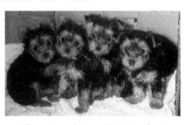

DEDICATION

To my wonderful wife Susan and my three adorable children - Nadia, Rebecca and David.

PREFACE

Keeping your Yorkshire Terrier healthy is the most important job that you, as owner, can do. Whereas there are many books available that deal with breed qualities, conformation, and show characteristics, this may be the only book available dedicated entirely to the preventive health care of the Yorkshire Terrier. This information has been compiled from a variety of sources and assembled here to provide you with the most up-to-date advice available.

This book will take you through the important stages of selecting your pet, screening it for inherited medical and behavioral problems, meeting its nutritional needs, and seeing that it receives optimal medical care.

So, enjoy the book and use the information to keep your Yorkshire Terrier the healthiest it can be for a long, full, and rich life.

Lowell Ackerman DVM